Contents

GW00319470

THE ANALYSIS OF COMMERCIAL VEHICLE STRUCTURES

Hans Joachim Beermann *was born in 1930. Educated from 1949–1954 at what is now the Technical University of Braunschweig, FRG, followed by two years as a research engineer with Professor P. Koeßler he received Dr.-Ing. From 1956–1959 he was at Daimler Benz AG and became head of the heavy truck test department. After a year at a Technical Inspection Organization he became senior research engineer at the Institute for Vehicle Technology at the Technical University of Braunschweig dealing with vehicle dynamics. Since 1970 he has been Professor and head of the Department of Vehicle Structures at that University.*

Guy Tidbury *was educated at Imperial College in Physics and Aeronautics and spent 15 years in the Aircraft Industry as an aerodynamicist and flight test engineer. The last 10 years of this period he was involved in the design and testing of helicopters. The years 1956–1960 were spent as a development engineer in the commercial vehicle section of Vauxhall Motors Ltd (Bedford trucks and Vans). In 1960 he participated in the founding of the Advanced School of Automobile Engineering at the then College of Aeronautics at Cranfield as the lecturer responsible for vehicle structures, becoming a senior lecturer in 1965. Later he became Director of Studies in Vehicle Structures in the School of Automotive Studies which was formed when Cranfield became an Institute of Technology. When the School was disbanded in 1983 he continued the work as Director of the Cranfield Impact Centre until retirement.*

The Analysis of Commercial Vehicle Structures

by
H. J. Beermann
English Translation Edited by
Guy Tidbury

Verlag TUV Rheinland GmbH
KOLN
Mechanical Engineering Publications Limited
LONDON

First published (in German) 1986
© Verlag TUV Rheinland GmbH, Koln

English language Edition 1989
© Mechanical Engineering Publications Limited

ISBN 0 85298 701 3

British Library Cataloguing in Publication Data

Beermann, H. J., *1930–*
    The analysis of commercial vehicle structures.
    1. Commercial vehicles. Chassis. Analysis & design.
    Applications of computer systems.
    I. Title   II. Tidbury, Guy   III. Rechnerische Analyse
    von Nutzfahrzeugtragwerken. *English*
    629.2'4

    ISBN 0-85298-701-3

Photoset by Paston Press, Loddon, Norfolk
Printed in Great Britain by
St Edmundsbury Press Limited, Bury St Edmunds, Suffolk

Editor's Preface

It is perhaps no coincidence that the vehicle structures groups at Cranfield and Braunschweig developed a similar interest in the problems of the analysis of commercial vehicle chassis frames. These apparently simple structures pose difficult and interesting problems. Both schools emphasised the importance of a thorough understanding of thin-walled beam theory in dealing with these problems during truck and trailer design and development. At the time of writing, most companies and all academic institutions accept this importance, and many of the latter have contributed to the application of the theory to this type of frame structure. The first paper to attempt to deal with the problem of partial warping inhibition in truck frames was written for the 1968 FISITA conference by Cranfield and, in a rudimentary way, used the basic idea of a force method to analyse the whole frame, with an approximation for the effect of the joints. In spite of occasional efforts to expand this work by student projects there, it has been left to the Braunschweig school, with properly funded continuous work by the author and his collaborators, to arrive at the practical solutions given in this book.

This book first summarises the theory and later incorporates it into a special computer analysis. The most important contribution of this work is the method of allowing for the different axes defining thin-walled beams meeting at joints. While several other writers have explored the idea of using different finite element programs for analysing the joints and the main framework, the author has succeeded in integrating this treatment with the problem of the axes and providing a consistent and usable system for the complete analysis of chassis frames, which has previously only been available from a study of papers from various sources.

In the case of buses, Cranfield concentrated on the 'rollover' safety problem, while Braunschweig worked mainly on the analysis of the structure for running loads. The method adopted for this analysis is also new in that it divides an apparently integral tubular framework into an underbody structure and a superstructure, which can be analysed separately and then combined. This approach will also be useful for those designing buses with separate chassis frames, even if they are 'soft' frames which are not self-supporting.

Although the author does not advise the widespread use of the theories of the deformation of the cross section of rectangular thin-walled tubes in torsion in the analysis of bus structures he does provide a much more understandable treatment of this theory than is generally available. In fact the theoretical part of the book will be of value far beyond the boundaries of vehicle structural engineering and will be useful for civil and mechanical engineers involved with all types of thin-walled framework structures.

In editing the translation I have retained the notation and figures used in the original German edition; however, in some cases the direct translation of the definition of the symbols does not correspond with the normal British usage. As far as possible I have agreed suitable definitions with the author. The main difference is in the theory of warping of open-section thin-walled beams where ω is defined as 'unit warping' or 'unit warping displacement'. This definition refers to the fact that it is the warping displacement or deformation due to unit rate of twist. It is the same as the parameter usually called the 'principal sectorial area', twice the area swept by a vector from the torsion centre to the centre line of the profile of the section when certain conditions are met for defining the zero point on the profile. Again, the section constant defined in the book as 'torsion constant due to warping' is defined by Vlassov as the 'second moment of sectorial area'. In the same way the title of chapter 5, 'Warping of open-section thin-walled beams', implies the whole theory usually involved with this problem, including bimoments and the associated twisting of the beams, etc. The concepts of 'zero warping lines' and the 'zero warping axis' in a cross section have been introduced by the editor for clarification of the author's argument, and have been approved by him. There are other cases where it has been necessary to invent definitions which are not usually defined in British text books, although I have not been able to conduct a thorough search of all possible sources.

In order to simplify printing, the equations have all been retained in the same order with their original numbering sequence. This constraint has meant that the original has had to be translated almost sentence by sentence, which prevented the restructuring of sections of the text which could have improved the readability of the English edition.

Thanks are due to Elke Sadeghi for the original translation of the book, and for her willingness to discuss the problems encountered in editing the unfamiliar sections. I am also indebted to Jason Brown of the Cranfield Impact Centre who read the work with great care and made several suggestions which have clarified the theoretical treatment, as well as acting as a second editor. Finally, the author has corrected the first draft of the translation and clarified some points which were not clear in the original. He has also introduced two figures and a small section of text to clarify the classical analysis of box beams.

Editing this work has been of great interest and satisfaction, and although it is essentially a theoretical book, I am sure that it will prove a valuable guide to the design of better vehicle structures.

Guy Tidbury

Foreword to the First Edition

The static and dynamic analysis of complex structures can be accomplished by the use of currently available computer programs where they can be described by a fine mesh of finite elements. The load-bearing chassis frames of commercial vehicles and trailers, as well as integral bus structures, can always be analysed by these programs. The results of such analyses should give an insight into the load distribution in the various members of the structure so that a desirable load distribution can be arrived at gradually in the process of design.

If superficial, and probably incorrect, estimates of the load distribution are to be avoided, calculations must be made, and these calculations can be arranged to give the required insight into the behaviour of the structure. By way of an example, the load–deformation characteristics and stress distribution in commercial vehicle frames cannot be properly understood if the effect of warping when the vehicle is subject to torsion is disregarded. With a comprehensive finite element idealisation such frames could be analysed, and the analysis would include the effect of warping, but the results would not clearly point out the effects of warping which dominate the torsion case. For bus structures it is useful to understand the way the superstructure and the underfloor structure combine to carry the load, and this would be masked in a comprehensive finite element analysis of the whole structure.

The methods of calculation given in this book for the analysis of commercial vehicle structures go beyond the conventional finite element systems and, with smaller programs, render the load distribution more comprehensible. Good experimental verification of the results is also demonstrated. The book outlines the theoretical basis of the computational methods proposed including the transfer matrix method which is useful for some special problems. This is followed by the theory of warping or deplanation of thin-walled beams of both open and closed sections, which is especially formulated to lead to the flexibility and stiffness matrices required in the analysis.

Commercial vehicle frames typically have short beams with extensive joints or nodal areas; consequently, the connections between the beams which are normally taken in analyses as either fixed or free joints have to be analysed separately in detail to ensure compatibility of the displacements and equilibrium of the forces at the ends of the beams. The nodal areas are therefore analysed as sub-structures by finite element methods which also give the detailed stresses in the nodal areas. Since finite element program systems are so well known they are only briefly discussed in this book, and a short chapter is sufficient to describe the coupling of the substructures and the beams.

Simplified approximate methods are given first, based on the fundamental principles previously described, and these have some value for quick assessment of designs; for example, they should be used to find the sizes of members for use in the detailed analysis methods given in later chapters. Finally, a chapter is devoted to the analysis of framework bus structures.

Since formulae are only useful if the symbols used can readily be found, the patience of the reader should not be tried by having to make a long search for the meaning of a particular symbol. For this reason great emphasis has been placed on the provision of a comprehensive list of symbols.

The fundamental principles of the stress analysis of chassis frames, and especially the methods of calculation presented in this work, were developed with the sponsorship and encouragement of the Deutschen Forschungsgemeinschaft (German Research Association), and I would like to take this opportunity to offer them my thanks. I would also like to thank my former collaborators Dr-Ing. H. Oehlschlaeger, Dr-Ing. U. Gohrbandt, and Dr-Ing. M. Marótzy, as well as my collaborators, Dipl-Ing. R. Schuller and Dipl-Ing. D. Lehmann, for their work and assistance in the theoretical analyses and in the experimental verification of the methods described in this work, as well as for checking the manuscript of the book. Thanks are also due to Mr G. Danzfuss for drawing the many illustrations and Mrs H. Müller who prepared the manuscript with patience and care.

H. J. Beermann

List of symbols

a	Function defined in equation (6.19); Influence coefficient; Length of side of a rectangular panel; Coefficient of the acceleration due to gravity; Distance between the forces in a couple
A	Cross sectional area; Suspension load
b	Width of frame; Width of cross section; Width of rectangular panel; Influence coefficient
B	Bimoment
B_{QI}	Transfer bimoment
c	Spring stiffness
c_S	Lozenging stiffness due to lateral bending
c_T	Torsional stiffness
c_V	Rate of twist stiffness
d	Influence coefficient; Distances defined in Fig. 8.3; Displacement
D	Lateral bimoment; Drawbar load
e	Distance
e_T	Distance between the torsion centre and the web of a channel section
E	Modulus of elasticity
f	Tangential displacement at a point on a cross section profile; Deformation of cross section; Displacement defined in Fig. 13.5
F	Force
g	Displacement defined in Fig. 13.5; Acceleration due to gravity
G	Shear modulus
h	Height; Height of cross section
h_S	Distance between the centroid axes of beams meeting at a joint
h_T	Vertical distance between the torsion axes of beams meeting at a joint
h_{Rd}	Wheel bump height
H	Horizontal force
J	Second moment of area

J_t	St Venant torsion constant
J_t^*	Effective torsion constant of beam with inhibition of warping
J_t^{**}	Effective torsion constant for dynamic case
J_ω	Torsion constant due to warping
k	Function defined in equation (6.36); Element number; Bay number; Node number
l	Length; Wheelbase
l_Q, l_{QI}	Length of cross member, see Fig. 8.7
l_x, m_x, n_x	Direction cosines defined in equation (4.43)
m	Number of cross members in chassis frame; Mass
M	Bending moment
M_D	Torque
M_K	Bending moment at centre of rear cross member due to drawbar load
M_R	Torque acting on chassis frame
M_t	St Venant torque
M_ω	Warping torque
n	Order of redundancy; Number of cross members; Number of point loads
N	Direct load; End load
P	Wheel load
q	Shear flow; Effective dynamic stiffness in nodal transfer matrices
Q	Shear force
r	Distance from shear centre to the tangent to the periphery of a thin-walled beam
r, s, t	Distances defined in Fig. 8.5
s	Distance along periphery; Number of elements in a system; Wheel track
S	Centroid; Side force
S_ω	Static warping moment
t	Thickness of shear panel; Thickness of thin walled beam; Time
T	Torsion centre
u	Displacement in x direction; Displacement of the node of a finite element; Longitudinal displacement in transfer matrix
u_K	Warping of rectangular beam
U	Length of periphery; Generalised load

v	Displacement in y direction; Lateral displacement in transfer matrix
V	Volume; Cross section deformation; Connecting force
V_1	Generalised rotational displacement
V_2	Generalised lozenging displacement
w	Displacement in z direction; Warping displacement; Influence coefficient
W	Warping point; Generalised warping displacement; Work due to displacement; Section modulus
X	Statically indeterminate force
x, y, z	Cartesian coordinates
X, Y, Z	Forces in coordinate directions
α	Warping constant defined in equation (5.29); Torsional displacement at a node
β	Slope due to bending
γ	Shear strain; Angle of lateral bending
δ	Displacement across a cut in a statically indeterminate system; Angle of rotation of a rigid panel
δ_{LQF}	Rate of twist flexibility of a node or joint
δ_{BQF}	Bending flexibility of a node or joint
δ_v	Virtual displacement of a node of an element
ε	Angle of pitch; Direct strain
ζ_1	Displacement function of rotation
ζ_2	Displacement function of lozenging of the cross section
η	Coefficient defined in equation (5.30)
ϑ	Angle of twist at any point along a beam; Rate of twist
μ	Coefficient of friction
ν	Poissons ratio
ρ	Flexibility of a beam with end load defined in equations (4.3)–(4.6)
σ	Direct stress
τ	Shear stress
Θ	Mass moment of inertia
φ	Angle of rotation; Angle of twist
χ	Warping displacement function
ψ	Constant defined in equation (12.37)
ω	Unit warping displacement; Unit warping; Eigenfrequency

Matrices are shown by bold letters; Transposed matrices by superscript ^{T}; Capital letters indicate rectangular matrices, e.g., $\mathbf{B}$; small letters indicate column matrices, e.g., $\mathbf{f}$; row matrices are shown as transposed column matrices, e.g., $\mathbf{f}^T$.

The following brackets indicate the different matrices:

[ ]	Normal matrix
⌊ ⌋	Diagonal matrix
{ }	Column matrix
{ }^{T}	Row matrix

$\mathbf{B}$	Internal load matrix–columns are internal loads due to unit external loads
$\mathbf{B}_0$	Matrix of internal loads in basic systems due to unit external loads
$\mathbf{B}_1$	Matrix of internal loads in basic systems due to unit statically indeterminate loads
$\mathbf{C}$	Coupling matrix; Damping matrix
$\mathbf{d}$	Matrix of node displacements
$\mathbf{d}_F$	Displacements corresponding to external loads
$\mathbf{D}_F$	Matrix of the rate of twist flexibilities of nodes
$\mathbf{f}$	Matrix of forces at the nodes; Matrix of internal element loads
$\mathbf{f}_F$	Matrix of external loads
$\mathbf{F}$	Overall flexibility matrix
$\mathbf{F}_h$	Element flexibility matrix
$\mathbf{F}_k$	Transfer matrix of the kth bay
$\mathbf{F}_v$	Diagonal matrix of the elements $\mathbf{F}_h$
$\mathbf{F}_F$	Overall flexibility matrix corresponding to the external forces
$\mathbf{I}$	Unit matrix
$\mathbf{K}$	Overall stiffness matrix
$\mathbf{K}_F$	Overall stiffness matrix corresponding to the external forces
$\mathbf{K}_h$	Element stiffness matrix
$\mathbf{K}_P$	Diagonal matrix of the element stiffness matrices $\mathbf{K}_h$
$\mathbf{M}$	Mass matrix
$\mathbf{p}$	Matrix of internal loads
$\mathbf{T}$	Transformation matrix between global and element coordinates; Joint transformation matrix
$\mathbf{T}_{x,y,z}$	Defined in equation (4.44)
$\mathbf{u}$	Displacement of nodes
$\mathbf{U}$	Nodal transfer matrix

List of symbols

v	Internal displacements of nodal points; Nodal element displacements
w	Matrix of deflections
x	Matrix of statically indeterminate loads
X	Matrix of statically indeterminate loads–the columns are due to external unit loads; Modal matrix
z	Matrix of state variables

Subscripts and superscripts

O	Referring to basic system; Referring to circular cross section
(O)	Referring to overall displacements including rigid body displacements
1	Referring to axles; Due to statically indeterminate load X_1
2	Referring to vehicle body structure; Due to statically indeterminate load X_2
a	Referring to bus superstructure
A	Referring to trailer; Referring to bus superstructure; Due to a support load
b	Referring to bus underfloor box girder structure
B	Referring to bus underfloor structure, see Fig. 13.8
c	Referring to bus cross member
d	Referring to displacement
f	Referring to stresses
h	Referring to element number h
H	Referring to rear axle; Sub-frame
i, j, k	Referring to the general point i, j, k
k	Number of a bay; One boundary of a bay (transfer matrices); Referring to node k
l, r	Left; Right
L	Referring to a side member
NM	Referring to direct force and bending moment
P	Referring to load carrying platform body
Q	Referring to cross member
Ql	Referring to bimoment hinge
R	Referring to chassis frame; Referring to rigid bodies
Rb	Referring to bending in plane of chassis frame
Rt	Referring to torsion in chassis frame
s	Referring to substructure s
St	Referring to forces due to vehicle pitching

t	Referring to St Venant torsion
V	Referring to front axle
Wt	Referring to warping due to torsion
x y z	Referring to cartesian directions
Z	Referring to towing vehicle
ω	Referring to warping

Abbreviations

Q	Cross member
L	Side member
^	Referring to global coordinates
S	Centroid
T	Torsion centre

1

Introduction

All vehicles are subject to both static and dynamic loads which cause stresses which are limited by the design life chosen for the structure of the vehicle. The dynamic properties of the structure also influence the level of stresses.

The static analysis of the structure gives, on the one hand, the internal loads in the structural elements making up the structure (e.g., the direct loads, normal loads, bending moments, and torque acting on the ends of the tubes making up a bus frame) due to instantaneous external loads, and on the other hand, the internal and external displacements caused by the load system. The internal loads can be arranged in a column matrix, $\mathbf{p}$, and the external loads in a column matrix, $\mathbf{f}$, while the structural deformations can be displayed in a column matrix, $\mathbf{d}$, consisting of displacements of the nodes joining the structural elements or the nodes of a finite element idealization of the structure. The analysis is carried out with the usual assumptions of small displacements and linear elasticity – the large deformations caused by vehicle impacts are not dealt with in this work. The basic equations relating these matrices are

$$\mathbf{p} = \mathbf{Bf} \tag{1.1}$$

and

$$\mathbf{f} = \mathbf{Kd} \tag{1.2}$$

with the internal load matrix, $\mathbf{B}$, and the stiffness matrix, $\mathbf{K}$, to be determined later. The latter is normally used as an inverted matrix, as in

$$\mathbf{d} = \mathbf{K}^{-1}\mathbf{f} \tag{1.2a}$$

The matrices $\mathbf{B}$ and $\mathbf{K}$ represent the static properties of a structure. To determine the dynamic properties, a mass matrix, $\mathbf{M}$, is also necessary. This matrix represents the statically equivalent distribution of the total mass concentrated at the nodes – a lumped mass idealization. An approximation to the damping properties is also made in the damping matrix $\mathbf{C}$.

The dynamic displacements can then be found from the relation

1

$$\mathbf{M\ddot{d}} + \mathbf{C\dot{d}} + \mathbf{Kd} = \mathbf{f}(t) \qquad (1.3)$$

The structural damping is normally small and can be approximated by viscous damping terms in $\mathbf{C}$. Considerable damping is found in external coupling devices, such as the connections between the chassis and body. In the case of the masses also, except for local oscillations, the chassis has a small effect compared with the laden body, as can be seen by comparing the weight of the bare chassis with the sprung vehicle weight. In equation (1.3), therefore, the stiffness matrix, $\mathbf{K}$, i.e., the force–deformation behaviour, is the dominant property of the structure.

In the case of frameworks such as chassis frames or bus structures, the stress–displacement relationship of the elements employed, expressed in the flexibility and stiffness matrices, is exact. When open cross-section, thin-walled beams (channel or 'I' sections) are used it is essential to include the effect of warping. For the behaviour of the whole structure the properties of the joints are as important as those of the beams joining them. The joint behaviour can only be approximated by the use of finite element idealizations, which, after being used to find the loads in the combined system, can be used for the analysis of the stresses in the area of the joint.

It is of paramount importance that experimental verification be provided for any mathematical structural analysis; this is especially true when new methods are being developed, and such evidence is produced in the text. In general it has been found that the static and dynamic behaviour of a structure can be satisfactorily calculated using a lower level of idealization than that required for analysing stress distributions, and this is further demonstrated in this work.

Commercial vehicle structures

The term 'commercial vehicle' is used here to describe all commercial vehicles (including buses), trailers, and semi-trailers. Buses normally have self supporting superstructures while trucks and trailers normally have chassis frames as the intrinsic load-carrying framework. Light vans and some pickups are exceptions to this generalization. The structural behaviour of the frame is also dependent on the structural characteristics of any superstructure attached to it. Such superstructures are categorized as non-self-supporting commercial vehicle structures. Chassis frames can be considered structurally as grillages. They offer the designer convenient arrangements for mounting other chassis components, superstructures (e.g., cabs) or subframes (e.g., a fifth wheel coupling). These ladder frames differ in the design of cross members and side members between trucks and trailers. In the case of trucks the design of some of the cross members is determined by the driveline components (e.g., engine cross member and rear axle cross member), while the load carrying body is normally carried by an additional frame. Trailer frames generally have more cross members which are lighter and extend to the sides the floor of the loading area to carry the load directly without separate body mounting frames. In the case of semi-trailers the side members are connected by strong cross members above the axles and fifth wheel coupling.

Grillages are plane frameworks loaded normal to their plane and in their plane, therefore the most obvious method of analysis is by a system of beam elements. The joints are often so large in comparison with the lengths of the beam elements, which are taken as the cross members and the sections of the side members between the cross members, that it is necessary to take into account the elastic properties of the joints. These elastic properties can be obtained by a finite element idealization of the joint area using shell elements. Cross members can have variable cross section over their length or can be curved, say, under the engine, and in these cases it is also necessary to use a finite element calculation to obtain the load–displacement properties of the cross members themselves. It has been shown by comparing theoretical and measured results that beam elements with uniform cross sections should not be analysed by using standard finite element programs as they lead to unacceptable approximations.

Bus structures are usually self-supporting frameworks (integral construction) with metal cladding and glazing areas which contribute to the strength and stiffness of the whole structure. The contribution of the metal skin depends on the method of attachment to the framework and the pre-tension of the skin. Since glass is very stiff in shear compared to the frame surrounding it, the glazing has a much larger effect on the framework than the skin, if it is attached by an adhesive. Traditional rubber glazing strip allows for some flexibility between the glass and the frame, but the stiffening effect of the glass is still considerable. Apart from complete integral bus structures, some designs incorporate a torsionally stiff underfloor framework of closed section members capable of carrying the required loads.

In general, the most important part of commercial vehicle structural analysis is the calculation of the framework characteristics, including the properties of the joints between the thin walled beams comprising either the chassis frame of a truck or trailer or the three dimensional framework of a bus.

3

Load cases

Whilst adequate durability under dynamic conditions is a design requirement for vehicle structures, the static load cases cannot be disregarded.
The following list of static loads, which should be taken as stressing cases,
includes maximum dynamic loads which only occur infrequently.

Load Case I	Static load of stationary vehicle
Load Case IIa	Braking
Load Case IIb	Acceleration
Load Case III	Cornering
Load Case IV	Torsion
Load Case Va	Maximum load on front axle
Load Case Vb	Maximum load on rear axle
Load Case VI	Drawbar loads
Load Case VII	Asymmetrical longitudinal loads from non-steering twin axles, or from unequal adhesion of the right and left hand wheel tracks under braking

The values for the individual load cases are taken from the expected
service conditions of the particular vehicle. The worst-case loading
conditions (distribution of load) as well as overloading must be considered
for the static load case. The braking and acceleration cases are determined
by the possible driving conditions (e.g., max. braking, engine power,
etc.). The lateral acceleration in cornering will be determined by the tyre
forces available, or a tilt test may be specified.

In the case of torsionally flexible vehicles such as trucks the maximum
torsion case is determined by the height of a bump on which one wheel is
resting when the other wheels are on a flat surface. The torque applied
depends on the torsional stiffness of the structure as well as the roll
stiffness of the suspension systems, as shown in chapter 12. In the case of
torsionally stiff vehicles, such as integral buses, the applied torque
depends only on the roll stiffness of the suspension systems, and the
maximum torsion case is found when one wheel of the most lightly loaded
axle is hanging free while the other is on a bump and both wheels of the
other axle are on a flat surface.

The maximum loads on the front and rear axles are balanced by inertia forces. These contrast with the factors usually applied to the static load case, especially for those vehicles with a long overhang containing concentrated loads (e.g., rear-engined buses). Such loads result in high bending moments over the rear axle, as shown in chapter 13.

The drawbar loads from the trailer coupling system are usually taken by the rear cross member and largely depend on the weights of the tractor and trailer.

The asymmetrical longitudinal loads can arise from different friction forces in the off-side and near-side wheel tracks. If the difference in friction force is taken as half the maximum friction obtainable (e.g. $\Delta \mu = 0.5$ if $\mu = 1$) then the maximum yawing moment which can occur with unsteered twin axles is less than that due to the asymmetric loads.

Dynamic loads result from inertia forces arising from driving on uneven surfaces. In the resulting equations of motion the stiffness matrix is obtained from the static analysis of the structure. The idealization of the mass distribution in the elements should be based on the strain distribution in the elements assumed for the finite element stress analysis, a consistent mass idealization. In practice, however, it is sufficient to use a lumped mass approximation, with simple statically equivalent masses concentrated at selected nodal points. Discrete attached masses are connected to the structure at the nodal points. The dynamic loads are obtained from an assumed or measured random road surface unevenness, as shown in reference (10).†

†References are given at the end of the book.

4

Methods of analysis

The analysis of the vehicle structures dealt with in this book requires both the determination of the behaviour of thin-walled beam elements in frameworks and more general global analysis methods. It is more advantageous to deal with the global analysis first, as the requirement to analyse the thin-walled beams arises automatically from this. The thin-walled beam analysis also involves a rather lengthy derivation compared with the global case.

4.1 EQUILIBRIUM AND COMPATIBILITY

The aim of a static analysis is to determine the internal loads and displacements of a structure when subjected to external loads. The basis for this analysis is that the equilibrium of forces and the compatibility of displacements shall be maintained at all points in the structure. In the dynamic case these conditions must also be maintained at all times. Since the term 'compatibility' can have many definitions it is necessary to state that it is the compatibility of displacements in the complete structural system that is meant here. The conditions of equilibrium and compatibility are sufficient for the direct analysis of statically determinate structures, such as pin-jointed frameworks, frameworks with shear panels, and frameworks without closed rings.

The equilibrium conditions for the forces X Y Z in the coordinate directions and the moments M_x M_y M_z acting about these coordinates give

$$\Sigma X = 0; \quad \Sigma Y = 0; \quad \Sigma Z = 0 \qquad (4.1a)$$

$$\Sigma M_x = 0; \quad \Sigma M_y = 0; \quad \Sigma M_z = 0 \qquad (4.1b)$$

It is preferable to define these forces at the nodal points or the joints. This results in the forces being defined at the ends of the beams, which allows for the inclusion of continuously varying direct loads and distributed normal loads along the beam. The analysis finds the internal loads at any point along the beam. The internal loads are given as stress distributions in the cross section of the beam. In the case of thin-walled, open-section beams the stress distribution includes the stresses due to the bi-moment as well as the customary stress distributions due to end loads, normal loads, bending moments, and torsion; see Chapter 5. Considerable loads can also occur from the deformation of the cross section of closed sections where the stress distribution is due to the lateral bi-moment which will be defined later. According to St Venant's principle, the stress distribution at any point along a beam can only be found at a sufficient distance from a joint or a point where an external load is introduced. Since the stresses in the vicinity of a joint, especially at the boundary between the joint and the beam element, are very important, the analysis of the structure based on the internal loads as defined above is only approximate, but it gives a very clear picture of the load distribution in the structure.

The compatibility condition, i.e., the condition that cohesion is maintained in the deformed structure, must be satisfied. The corresponding displacement at a point i when a unit load is applied at point k follows from the well known principle of virtual forces, as given by the equation

$$d_{ik} = \sum_h \int^{\varrho_h} U_{ih}U_{kh}\, d\varrho \qquad (4.2)$$

Where U_{ih} and U_{kh} are the internal loads in element h due to unit loads at i and k, respectively.

The flexibilities of an element for the various internal loads are as follows

$$\text{Direct Loads} \qquad U_h \equiv N_h \qquad \varrho_h = \frac{l_h}{EA_h} \qquad (4.3)$$

$$\text{Bending Moments} \qquad U_h \equiv M_h \qquad \varrho_h = \frac{l_h}{EJ_h} \qquad (4.4)$$

$$\text{Torques} \qquad U_h \equiv M_{Dh} \qquad \varrho_h = \frac{l_h}{GJ_{th}} \qquad (4.5)$$

$$\text{Shear Flows} \qquad U_h \equiv q_h \qquad \varrho_h = \frac{a_h b_h}{Gt_h} \qquad (4.6)$$

with N being the direct load, M the bending moment, M_D the torque, q the shear flow, l the length of beam element, A the cross section area, J the second moment of area, J_t the St Venant torsion constant, a and b the lengths of the sides of a rectangular shear panel, and t the thickness of the panel. The significant internal loads which contribute to the work of deformation of the structure are the direct loads in the members of pin-jointed frameworks, bending moments and torques in the beams of rigid jointed frameworks, and shear flows and direct loads in frameworks with shear panels.

In equation (4.2) the product $U_{kh}\varrho_h$ is the internal displacement due to the unit load at k. This can be demonstrated by using the simple example of a pin-jointed framework. Since in this case the direct load is constant along the length of each beam and is the only load present, the displacement at any point can be expressed as the sum

$$d_{ik} = \Sigma_h U_{ih} U_{kh}\varrho_h$$

Using equation (4.3) and the usual definition of strain, $\varepsilon = \sigma/E$,

$$U_{kh}\varrho_h = \frac{U_{kh}}{EA_h} l_h = \varepsilon_h l_h = \Delta l_h$$

Besides the requirement that the internal loads, U_{ih}, and the external unit load, i, should be equivalent, the principle of virtual work demands that the external and internal displacements be compatible, i.e., d_{ik} and the internal displacement Δl_n.

Redundant or statically indeterminate structures are analysed on the basis of equilibrium conditions and the compatibility of elastic deformations. A basic or statically determinate system is created by making a number of cuts equal to the order of redundancy of the structure. From the compatibility condition the displacement across each cut must be zero. Hence the redundant forces must be such as to close the corresponding cuts. The compatibility equations become

$$\delta_{10} + \delta_{11}X_1 + \delta_{12}X_2 + \ldots = 0$$
$$\delta_{20} + \delta_{21}X_1 + \delta_{22}X_2 + \ldots = 0 \qquad (4.7)$$
$$\vdots$$

where δ_{10} is the displacement across the cut where the redundant force X_1 acts due to the external loads, δ_{11} is the change in the same displacement caused by a unit redundant force ($X_1 = 1$), δ_{12} is the change in the same displacement due to the unit redundant force ($X_2 = 1$), etc. The displacements δ are calculated from equation (4.2) where δ is substituted for d and represents both rotational and translational displacements.

The amount of work involved in the analysis of a redundant structure depends on the choice of the basic system, as it is important that the redundant forces only cause internal loads in as small an area of the structure as possible. Simple redundant structures can be analysed easily using this method. In the case of simple frameworks, for instance, the method of Ritter's Sections may split the framework into a statically determinate part of the structure and a number of statically indeterminate sub-structures. However, matrix methods are preferred for the analysis of horizontal bending and torsion in vehicle chassis frames, as well as for the analysis of all the load cases in integral vehicle frameworks.

4.2 THE MATRIX FORCE METHOD

An important advantage of matrix methods over other methods of analysis is that only the load–displacement characteristics of the elements have to be calculated rather than those of the whole structure. In the case of frameworks the structure breaks up naturally into beam elements with the joints as nodes. As an example Fig. 4.1 shows a grillage with s beam elements. At each node there are three translations and three rotations as possible displacements (Fig. 4.1(b)) as well as three forces and three moments (Fig. 4.1(c)). These forces and moments are referred to as the

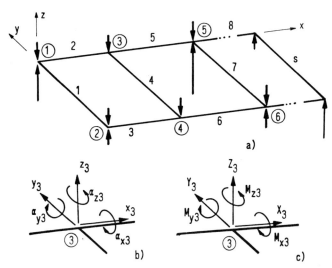

Fig. 4.1 (a) **Grillage in a horizontal plane subject to vertical loads**
           (b) **Possible displacements at a node**
           (c) **Forces at a node**

loads at a node. For the kth node the displacements and loads are arranged in column matrices

$$\mathbf{d}_k = \{x_k \ y_k \ z_k \ \alpha_{xk} \ \alpha_{yk} \ \alpha_{zk}\} \quad (4.8)$$

$$\mathbf{f}_k = \{X_k \ Y_k \ Z_k \ M_{xk} \ M_{yk} \ M_{zk}\} \quad (4.9)$$

and for the complete structure

$$\mathbf{d} = \{\mathbf{d}_1 \ \mathbf{d}_2 \ldots \mathbf{d}_k \ldots\} \quad (4.10)$$

$$\mathbf{f} = \{\mathbf{f}_1 \ \mathbf{f}_2 \ldots \mathbf{f}_k \ldots\} \quad (4.11)$$

The relation between the loads and displacements can be formulated in two ways

$$\mathbf{d} = \mathbf{F}\mathbf{f} \quad (4.12)$$

using the flexibility matrix $\mathbf{F}$, or

$$\mathbf{f} = \mathbf{K}\mathbf{d} \quad (4.13)$$

using the stiffness matrix $\mathbf{K}$. The matrix force method is based on the use of flexibility matrices while the matrix displacement method uses stiffness matrices.

Figure 4.2 shows the displacements and loads at the ends of a longitudinal beam element in the grillage. End 1 of the beam element is usually placed at the node in the global system with the lowest identification

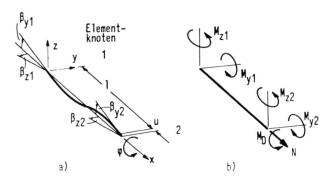

Fig. 4.2 **(a)** **Element coordinates and nodal displacements**
(b) **Element nodal loads**
In (a) 'Element-knoten 1' = 'End 1'.

number. From the figure the displacement and load column matrices are

$$\mathbf{v}_h = \{u_h \ \beta_{y1h} \ \beta_{y2h} \ \beta_{z1h} \ \beta_{z2h} \ \varphi_h\} \tag{4.14}$$

$$\mathbf{p}_h = \{N_h \ M_{y1h} \ M_{y2h} \ M_{z1h} \ M_{z2h} \ M_{Dh}\} \tag{4.15}$$

It will be noticed that normal loads with their associated displacements are not included, nor are the end load and torque at end 1. These follow from the equilibrium conditions of the beam element.

The load–displacement relation for the beam element is

$$\mathbf{v}_h \dot{} = \mathbf{F}_h \mathbf{p}_h \tag{4.16}$$

The element flexibility matrix $\mathbf{F}_h$ is made up from the well known flexibilities of a beam when simple torsion only is taken into account and is written out as

$$
\begin{bmatrix} u_h \\ \beta_{y1h} \\ \beta_{y2h} \\ \beta_{z1h} \\ \beta_{z2h} \\ \varphi_h \end{bmatrix}
=
\begin{bmatrix}
\dfrac{l_h}{EA_h} & & & & & \\[2ex]
& \dfrac{l_h}{3EJ_{yh}} & -\dfrac{l_h}{6EJ_{yh}} & & & \\[2ex]
& -\dfrac{l_h}{6EJ_{yh}} & \dfrac{l_h}{3EJ_{yh}} & & & \\[2ex]
& & & \dfrac{l_h}{3EJ_{zh}} & -\dfrac{l_h}{6EJ_{zh}} & \\[2ex]
& & & -\dfrac{l_h}{6EJ_{zh}} & \dfrac{l_h}{3EJ_{zh}} & \\[2ex]
& & & & & \dfrac{l_h}{GJ_{th}}
\end{bmatrix}
\begin{bmatrix} N_h \\ M_{y1h} \\ M_{y2h} \\ M_{z1h} \\ M_{z2h} \\ M_{Dh} \end{bmatrix}
$$

$$\tag{4.16a}$$

For thin walled, especially open section, beams this formulation is not sufficient as only the St Venant torsion constant is used. The actual torsional behaviour of this type of beam is dominated by the effect of warping in the case of open sections and by profile deformation in the case of closed sections. The theory for these additional torsion effects is given in chapters 5 and 6 while the enlarged flexibility matrices are derived in chapter 7.

For the complete structure the element flexibility matrices are arranged at this stage as a diagonal matrix $\mathbf{F}$

$$\mathbf{F_v} = \begin{bmatrix} \mathbf{F}_1 & & & & & \\ & \mathbf{F}_2 & & & & \\ & & \ddots & & & \\ & & & \mathbf{F}_h & & \\ & & & & \ddots & \\ & & & & & \mathbf{F}_s \end{bmatrix} \qquad (4.17)$$

with the loads and displacements at all the nodes being given by the column matrices

$$\mathbf{v} = \{v_1 v_2 \ldots v_h \ldots v_s\} \qquad (4.18)$$

$$\mathbf{p} = \{p_1 p_2 \ldots p_h \ldots p_s\} \qquad (4.19)$$

The nodal displacements of the elements $\mathbf{v}$ can be regarded as internal displacements and the loads at the ends of the beam elements $\mathbf{p}$ as the internal loads in the structure, therefore

$$\mathbf{v} = \mathbf{F_v p} \qquad (4.20)$$

Since there must be equilibrium between the internal and external loads it is convenient to express the external loads as a column matrix $\mathbf{f_F}$ to distinguish them from the column matrix of the possible nodal forces $\mathbf{f}$, which contains a large number of zeros, see Fig. 4.1 as an example. The displacements corresponding to the external loads can also be arranged as a column matrix $\mathbf{d_F}$.

Using a statically determinate basic system the internal loads can be expressed as

$$\mathbf{p} = \mathbf{B_0 f_F} + \mathbf{B_1 x} \qquad (4.21)$$

where the columns of $\mathbf{B_0}$ contain the internal loads in the elements due to unit external loads. There will, of course, be zeros corresponding to the internal loads not included in the basic system. The columns of $\mathbf{B_1}$ contain the internal loads due to unit redundant forces in turn. The column vector $\mathbf{x}$ contains the unknown redundant forces as

$$\mathbf{x} = \{X_1 X_2 \ldots X_h\} \qquad (4.22)$$

They are related to the external loads by

$$x = Xf_F \tag{4.23}$$

The matrix X contains the unknown redundant forces in terms of unit values of the external loads. Equation (4.21) can now be written as

$$p = (B_0 + B_1X)f_F \tag{4.24}$$

The fundamental work relationship equating the internal and external work can be expressed as

$$f_F^T d_F = p^T v \tag{4.25}$$

Similar work equations follow for statically equivalent groups of loads and their corresponding displacements, which must be compatible. The work done by the internal loads of the whole structure $p^T v$ and by the internal loads of the basic system $p_0^T v$ must both be the same as that done by the external loads, therefore

$$f_F^T d_F = p_0^T v \tag{4.26}$$

and, from equation (4.25)

$$p^T v = p_0^T v \tag{4.27}$$

from equation (4.24) and the definition of p_0 the following relations can be written

$$p_0 = B_0 f_F \tag{4.28}$$

$$f_F^T(B_0 + B_1X)^T v = f_F^T B_0^T v \tag{4.29}$$

using the internal displacements from equation (4.20) and (4.24) again, (4.29) becomes

$$f_F^T X^T B_1^T F_v (B_0 + B_1X)f_F = o \tag{4.30}$$

Since this relationship holds for the external loads

$$X^T(B_1^T F_v B_0 + B_1^T F_v B_1 X) = O \tag{4.31}$$

The first term in the bracket represents the displacements across the cuts where the redundant forces act in the basic system due to the unit external loads. The elements in the matrix correspond to the right hand side of equation (4.2). This can be seen by comparing them with the direct load terms in equation (4.16a). The second term represents the displacements across the cuts due to redundant forces caused by unit values of the external loads, see equation (4.23). The whole bracket in equation (4.31) represents the compatibility condition, therefore

$$\mathbf{B}_1^T \mathbf{F}_v \mathbf{B}_0 + \mathbf{B}_1^T \mathbf{F}_v \mathbf{B}_1 \mathbf{X} = \mathbf{O} \qquad (4.32)$$

It is from this equation that the unknown redundant forces $\mathbf{X}$ due to unit values of the external loads have to be found. The internal loads $\mathbf{p}$ then follow from (4.24).

The displacements $\mathbf{d}_F$ are related to the external loads $\mathbf{f}_F$ by the overall flexibility matrix $\mathbf{F}_F$ by

$$\mathbf{d}_F = \mathbf{F}_F \mathbf{f}_F \qquad (4.33)$$

Substituting this in equation (4.26) and $\mathbf{p}_0$ from equation (4.28), $\mathbf{v}$ from equation (4.20), and $\mathbf{p}$ from (4.24) gives

$$\mathbf{f}_F^T \mathbf{F}_F \mathbf{f}_F = \mathbf{f}_F^T \mathbf{B}_0^T \mathbf{F}_v (\mathbf{B}_0 + \mathbf{B}_1 \mathbf{X}) \mathbf{f}_F \qquad (4.34)$$

Since this applies to any external loads, the flexibility matrix becomes

$$\mathbf{F}_F = \mathbf{B}_0^T \mathbf{F}_v (\mathbf{B}_0 + \mathbf{B}_1 \mathbf{X}) \qquad (4.35)$$

In practice the displacements at nodal points, or joints, where there are no external loads may be required. To find these values $\mathbf{d}_F$ has to be enlarged by inserting zeros in $\mathbf{f}_F$ where there are no external loads.

In order to distinguish a statically determinate structure from the basic systems so far discussed the notation $\mathbf{B}_0^{(b)}$ is used instead of $\mathbf{B}_0$. The internal loads can be found simply from equation (4.28) as

$$\mathbf{p} = \mathbf{B}_0^{(b)} \mathbf{f}_F \qquad (4.36)$$

and the displacements can be found from (4.33) and (4.35) as

$$\mathbf{d}_F = \mathbf{B}_0^{(b)T} \mathbf{F}_v \mathbf{B}_0^{(b)} \mathbf{f}_F \qquad (4.37)$$

Structural analysis using the matrix force method requires the calculation of the element flexibilities in the matrix $\mathbf{F}_v$ as well as the formation of the matrices $\mathbf{B}_0$ and $\mathbf{B}_1$ which contain the result of statically determinate calculations. These three matrices together with equations (4.32), (4.24), (4.35), and (4.33) give all the internal loads and displacements. For statically indeterminate, or redundant, structures a statically determinate basic system has to be formed. [*Editor's Note.* For some structures the use of redundant basic systems may be necessary, see, for example, section

4.1.] The need to choose a basic system, together with the requirement that the internal loads of the whole structure have to be calculated, means that automatic methods of calculation are not simple to apply. This can be used to advantage in structures with a simple arrangement of elements, as, for example, in the case of commercial vehicle chassis frames. It is shown in chapter 12 that nodal flexibilities can be included easily in the compatibility equation (4.32). It is possible to choose redundant forces automatically in more complex structures using the Jordan elimination procedure; reference (12).

4.3   THE MATRIX DISPLACEMENT METHOD

The redundancies do not appear as separate unknowns in the matrix displacement method, which means that they do not have to be determined by the analyst. It is therefore suitable for the analysis of large statically indeterminate structures where the preparation of the data can be made more automatic than is the case with the matrix force method. The basic relationship used in the analysis is summarized in equation (4.13), namely

$$\mathbf{f} = \mathbf{Kd}$$

where the nodal displacements, $\mathbf{d}$, due to the external loads, $\mathbf{f}$, are calculated. This involves the inversion of the stiffness matrix, $\mathbf{K}$

For this method all the possible displacements and all the possible internal loads at the element nodes are required for the analysis. This is in contrast to the matrix force method where, as is shown in Fig. 4.2 and in equations (4.7) and (4.15), some of these quantities can be eliminated by the use of equilibrium conditions. For a beam element all the possible displacements and loads are shown in Fig. 4.3 and they can be expressed by the column matrices

$$\mathbf{v}_h = \{u_{1h}\ v_{1h}\ w_{1h}\ \varphi_{1h}\ \beta_{y1h}\ \beta_{z1h}\ u_{2h}\ v_{2h}\ w_{2h}\ \varphi_{2h}\ \beta_{y2h}\ \beta_{z2h}\} \quad (4.38)$$

$$\begin{aligned}\mathbf{p}_h = \{&N_{1h}\ Q_{y1h}\ Q_{z1h}\ M_{D1h}\ M_{y1h}\ M_{z1h}\\ &N_{2h}\ Q_{y2h}\ Q_{z2h}\ M_{D2h}\ M_{y2h}\ M_{z2h}\}\end{aligned} \quad (4.39)$$

which are related by the equation

$$\mathbf{p}_h = \mathbf{K}_h\mathbf{v}_h \quad (4.40)$$

where K_h is the element stiffness matrix, which is given in full by the symmetrical matrix in the equation

$$
\mathbf{K}_h = \frac{E}{l_h} \cdot
\begin{bmatrix}
A \\
& 12\dfrac{J_z}{l_h^2} \\
& & 12\dfrac{J_y}{l_h^2} \\
& & & \dfrac{G}{E}J_t \\
& & -6\dfrac{J_y}{l_h} & & 4J_y \\
& 6\dfrac{J_z}{l_h} & & & & 4J_z \\
-A & & & & & & A \\
& -12\dfrac{J_z}{l_h^2} & & & & -6\dfrac{J_z}{l_h} & & 12\dfrac{J_z}{l_h^2} \\
& & -12\dfrac{J_y}{l_h^2} & & 6\dfrac{J_y}{l_h} & & & & 12\dfrac{J_y}{l_h^2} \\
& & & -\dfrac{G}{E}J_t & & & & & & \dfrac{G}{E}J_t \\
& & -6\dfrac{J_y}{l_h} & & 2J_y & & & & 6\dfrac{J_y}{l_h} & & 4J_y \\
& 6\dfrac{J_z}{l_h} & & & & 2J_z & & -6\dfrac{J_z}{l_h} & & & & 4J_z
\end{bmatrix}
\qquad \text{symm.}
$$

$$(4.41)$$

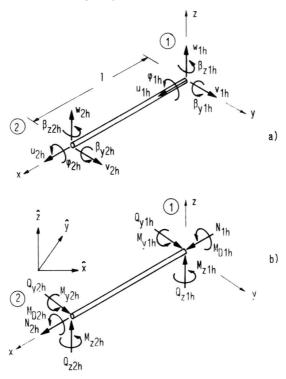

Fig. 4.3 (a) **All possible displacements of the nodes of beam element 'h'**
(b) **Nodal loads on beam element 'h'**

Since all the displacements, both of the elements and the complete structure, must fulfil compatibility conditions, they must be the same at each node for all elements meeting at the node, whether it is an internal or external node. For equilibrium conditions all the loads acting at a node, including the external loads where they act, must be in equilibrium. Compatibility and equilibrium are thus the basis for assembling the global stiffness matrix. The element stiffness matrix is in local or element coordinates and it must be transformed into the global coordinates designated by (ˆ) in Fig. 4.3.

The transformation matrix in the relationship

$$\mathbf{v}_h = \mathbf{T}\hat{\mathbf{v}}_h \tag{4.42}$$

is made up of the direction cosines between the element and global coordinates, defined in the usual way

$$
\begin{aligned}
l_x &= \cos(x, \hat{x}) & l_y &= \cos(y, \hat{x}) & l_z &= \cos(z, \hat{x}) \\
m_x &= \cos(x, \hat{y}) & m_y &= \cos(y, \hat{y}) & m_z &= \cos(z, \hat{y}) \\
n_x &= \cos(x, \hat{z}) & n_y &= \cos(y, \hat{z}) & n_z &= \cos(z, \hat{z})
\end{aligned} \tag{4.43}
$$

and

$$
\begin{aligned}
\mathbf{T}_x &= [l_x \; m_x \; n_x] \\
\mathbf{T}_y &= [l_y \; m_y \; n_y] \\
\mathbf{T}_z &= [l_z \; m_z \; n_z]
\end{aligned} \tag{4.44}
$$

for a beam element arbitrarily disposed in space this becomes

$$
\mathbf{T} = \begin{bmatrix}
\begin{matrix} \mathbf{T}_x \\ \mathbf{T}_y \\ \mathbf{T}_z \end{matrix} & 0 & 0 & 0 \\
0 & \begin{matrix} \mathbf{T}_x \\ \mathbf{T}_y \\ \mathbf{T}_z \end{matrix} & 0 & 0 \\
0 & 0 & \begin{matrix} \mathbf{T}_x \\ \mathbf{T}_y \\ \mathbf{T}_z \end{matrix} & 0 \\
0 & 0 & 0 & \begin{matrix} \mathbf{T}_x \\ \mathbf{T}_y \\ \mathbf{T}_z \end{matrix}
\end{bmatrix} \tag{4.45}
$$

or, more simply, for a beam element in a two dimensional structure

$$
\mathbf{T} = \begin{bmatrix}
\begin{matrix} l_x & m_x & 0 \\ l_y & m_y & 0 \\ 0 & 0 & 1 \end{matrix} & \mathbf{0} \\
\mathbf{0} & \begin{matrix} l_x & m_x & 0 \\ l_y & m_y & 0 \\ 0 & 0 & 1 \end{matrix}
\end{bmatrix} \tag{4.46}
$$

In order to use the principle of virtual work the transformation equation for the displacements of the nodes of the elements (4.42) is written as an equation of virtual displacements

$$\delta \mathbf{v}_h = \mathbf{T} \delta \hat{\mathbf{v}}_h \qquad (4.47)$$

The virtual work done at the nodes of the elements is independent of the coordinate system, so that

$$\delta \hat{\mathbf{v}}_h^T \hat{\mathbf{p}}_h = \delta \mathbf{v}_h^T \mathbf{p}_h \qquad (4.48)$$

combining this with equation (4.47) gives

$$\delta \hat{\mathbf{v}}_h^T \hat{\mathbf{p}}_h = \delta \hat{\mathbf{v}}_h^T \mathbf{T}^T \mathbf{p}_h \qquad (4.49)$$

which applies to any set of virtual displacements, so that the transformation of the nodal loads follows as

$$\hat{\mathbf{p}}_h = \mathbf{T}^T \mathbf{p}_h \qquad (4.50)$$

Multiplying both sides of equation (4.40) by $\mathbf{T}^T$ and substituting for $\mathbf{v}_h$ from equation (4.42), there follows

$$\mathbf{T}^T \mathbf{p}_h = \mathbf{T}^T \mathbf{K}_h \mathbf{T} \hat{\mathbf{v}}_h \qquad (4.51)$$

substituting into equation (4.50) gives

$$\hat{\mathbf{p}}_h = \mathbf{T}^T \mathbf{K}_h \mathbf{T} \hat{\mathbf{v}}_h \qquad (4.52)$$

Now the element stiffness matrix in global coordinates can be written as

$$\hat{\mathbf{K}}_h = \mathbf{T}^T \mathbf{K}_h \mathbf{T} \qquad (4.53)$$

The method of compiling the global stiffness matrix will be demonstrated for a plane framework or grillage as it is easier to understand than for a full three dimensional structure. For such a system the loads acting on the

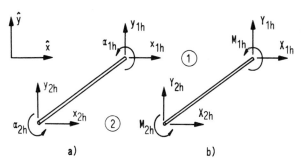

Fig. 4.4 (a) **Nodal displacements**
          (b) **Nodal loads for a beam element in a plane structure in global coordinates**

beam elements are specified at the ends of the beams in global coordinates, see Fig. 4.4 giving the column vector of loads

$$\hat{\mathbf{p}}_h = \{X_{1h}\ Y_{1h}\ M_{1h}\ X_{2h}\ Y_{2h}\ M_{2h}\} \qquad (4.54)$$

and the corresponding displacements

$$\hat{\mathbf{v}}_h = \{x_{1h}\ y_{1h}\ \alpha_{1h}\ x_{2h}\ y_{2h}\ \alpha_{2h}\} \qquad (4.55)$$

The element stiffness matrix is partitioned to separate the loads and displacements at each end of the beam, as shown in

$$
\begin{matrix}
 & \{x_{1h}\ y_{1h}\ \alpha_{1h}\ x_{2h}\ y_{2h}\ \alpha_{2h}\} & \hat{\mathbf{v}}_h \\
\begin{bmatrix} X_{1h} \\ Y_{1h} \\ M_{1h} \\ X_{2h} \\ Y_{2h} \\ M_{2h} \end{bmatrix} = & \begin{bmatrix} \mathbf{K}_h^{11} & \mathbf{K}_h^{12} \\ \hline \mathbf{K}_h^{21} & \mathbf{K}_h^{22} \end{bmatrix} & \\
\hat{\mathbf{p}}_h & & \hat{\mathbf{K}}_h
\end{matrix}
\qquad (4.56)
$$

[*Editor's note.* The notation used in this equation is not familiar as it is normally written as: column matrix $\hat{\mathbf{p}}_h$ equals $\hat{\mathbf{K}}_h$ multiplied by the column matrix $\hat{\mathbf{v}}_h$. In other words the column matrix arranged above the square matrix would normally be on the right of it. As this form is used extensively later in the book it becomes clear what is meant. It is analogous to the Cracovian form of the equation.]

The displacements $x_{1h}, y_{1h}, \ldots$ and element loads $X_{1h}, Y_{1h}, \ldots$, as well as the partitions $K_h^{11} \ldots$ of the stiffness matrix $\hat{\mathbf{K}}_h$ relate to the global coordinates, and from this point on all the formulae are based on global coordinates so that the special symbol (ˆ) will not be used to distinguish them.

The displacements at any node, k, in the structure can be written as

$$\mathbf{d}_k = \{x_k\ y_k\ \alpha_k\}$$

The displacements at the end of any beam element, h_k, meeting at the node k will be equal to the displacements of the structure at that node, so that the terms in $\mathbf{d}_k$ are

$$x_{1hk}\ y_{1hk}\ \alpha_{1hk} \quad \text{if end 1 of the beam element is at node } k$$

or

x_{2hk} y_{2hk} α_{2hk} if end 2 of the beam element is at node k

The loads from the beam h_k at node k when end 1 is at node k are

$$\{X_{1hk}\ \ Y_{1hk}\ \ M_{1hk}\} = \mathbf{K}_{hk}^{11}\mathbf{d}_k$$

the loads at end 2 of the same beam element are

$$\{X_{2hk}\ \ Y_{2hk}\ \ M_{2hk}\} = \mathbf{K}_{hk}^{21}\mathbf{d}_k$$

These loads affect the loads at the structural node where end 2 of the beam element is located.

If end 2 of a beam element is located at the structural node k the loads will be

$$\{X_{2hk}\ \ Y_{2hk}\ \ M_{2hk}\} = \mathbf{K}_{hk}^{22}\mathbf{d}_k$$

and at the other end the loads are

$$\{X_{1hk}\ \ Y_{1hk}\ \ M_{1hk}\} = \mathbf{K}_{hk}^{12}\mathbf{d}_k$$

The complete stiffness matrix is built up by arranging the partitioned element stiffness matrices in accordance with the above scheme. As an example of this procedure the section of a bus side wall is shown in Fig. 4.5, with two beam elements, 41 and 44, labelled as part of a finite element scheme. These two elements will have element stiffness matrices $\mathbf{K}_{41}$ and $\mathbf{K}_{44}$ as parts of the overall stiffness matrix $\mathbf{K}^{(0)}$ defined in

$$\mathbf{f}^{(0)} = \mathbf{K}^{(0)}\mathbf{d}^{(0)} \tag{4.57}$$

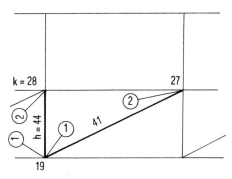

Fig. 4.5 **Example showing the arrangement of beam elements in bus side frame for insertion into the overall stiffness matrix**

This equation is built up as shown in Table 4.1.

Table 4.1 Arrangement of element stiffness matrices in the overall stiffness matrix

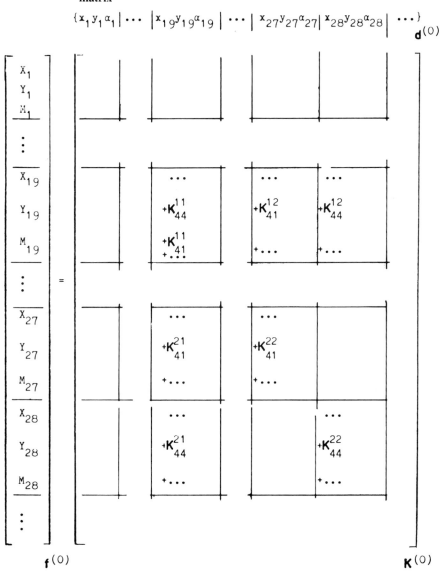

If the overall stiffness matrix $\mathbf{K}^{(0)}$ is assembled in this way, without taking the supports of the structure into account, it becomes singular. This is because all possible displacements of the structure are allowed and rigid body motion of the whole system can take place. This is prevented by defining rigid supports where the displacements are zero. The support system must be at least statically determinate. This is achieved mathematically by having zeros in the $\mathbf{d}^{(0)}$ matrix corresponding to the directions of zero displacement at the supports. When the rows and columns are omitted from the stiffness matrix, $\mathbf{K}^{(0)}$, it becomes the overall structural matrix, $\mathbf{K}$, of equation (4.13). The non-zero displacements in $\mathbf{d}$ due to the external loads are obtained by inverting the stiffness matrix, $\mathbf{K}$. The displacements of the ends of the elements are obtained by re-transforming $\mathbf{d}$ into element coordinates, resulting in the displacement vector, $\mathbf{v}_h$. Equation (4.40) then gives the loads in the elements, and these can be used to give the stress at any point in the structure.

If there are redundant supports the associated rows and columns in the $\mathbf{K}$ matrix have to be cancelled initially so that the analysis of the non-zero displacements in $\mathbf{d}$ can be made from the remaining system of equations. The support loads can be found by multiplying the rows corresponding to them in the $\mathbf{K}^{(0)}$ matrix by the displacement vector, $\mathbf{d}$.

4.4 TRANSFER MATRICES

The matrix methods of structural analysis described in the two previous sections are suitable for the analysis of frameworks consisting of beam elements. For some framework problems procedures using transfer matrices have advantages. The theory is presented very briefly here, concentrating on its use in the analysis of commercial vehicle chassis frames. As is well known, the basis of the theory was developed by Falk, but a practical presentation for use in civil engineering is given by Kersten (7).

In-plane bending of two-dimensional frames
As an example, Fig. 4.6 shows the lateral horizontal loads on a chassis frame of a commercial vehicle and the resulting bending moment diagram. The analysis uses the load–displacement relations, as well as the equilibrium and compatibility conditions of the beam elements to find the loads at one end of the frame from those at the other. The state variables are the displacements and the internal loads at the ends of the beams.

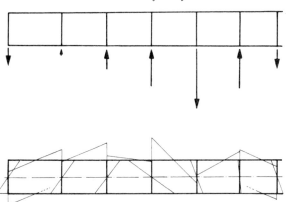

Fig. 4.6 Example of the lateral loads on a chassis frame due to cornering and the resulting bending moment diagram

These are compiled in a column matrix, sometimes called the state vector, which, for a beam in bending, has the form

$$\mathbf{z} = \{v \ \ \beta \ \ M \ \ Q \ \ 1\} \tag{4.58}$$

where v is the lateral displacement at the ends, β is the slope, M the bending moment, and Q the lateral or normal load (shear force) acting on the beam. The element '1' is added to include the external load, as will be shown later. Given the loads and displacements in the front cross member the state variables can be calculated for the next cross member by the use of transfer matrices. In fact, only some of the state variables at the front are known and the remainder depend on the boundary conditions at the rear end of the frame. Since the state variables at the rear are expressed in terms of those at the front, the structure can be analysed.

Figure 4.7 shows the loads and displacements at the ends of a beam element in the kth bay of the frame. Since the loads at a 'cut' are equal and opposite only those at the right hand side of the cut are defined. A clockwise moment at the right hand end of the beam therefore appears as an anticlockwise moment at the left hand end of the adjoining structure. The left hand end of the element is indicated by the suffixes kk and the other end by $kk + 1$. The relation between the state variables at the ends of the beam is given by

$$\mathbf{z}_{kk+1} = \mathbf{F}_k \mathbf{z}_{kk} \tag{4.59}$$

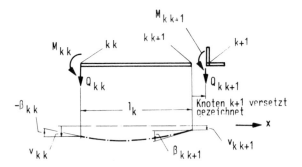

Fig. 4.7   State variables at the ends of a beam element in bending. [Note: node $k + 1$ shown separated]

with the transfer matrix

$$\mathbf{F}_k = \begin{bmatrix} 1 & -l_k & \dfrac{l_k^2}{2EJ_k} & \dfrac{l_k^3}{6EJ_k} & 0 \\[2ex] 0 & 1 & -\dfrac{l_k}{EJ_k} & -\dfrac{l_k^2}{2EJ_k} & 0 \\[2ex] 0 & 0 & 1 & l_k & 0 \\[2ex] 0 & 0 & 0 & 1 & 0 \\[2ex] 0 & 0 & 0 & 0 & 1 \end{bmatrix} \qquad (4.60)$$

the elements of this matrix are the load–deflection characteristics of a beam in bending.

Figure 4.8 shows, as an example, a 4 bay grillage acting as a simply supported beam with lateral loads at each cross member. While the supports shown at the ends may be fictitious, displacements can be measured from the line joining them. The right hand support is free to move in the longitudinal direction. In this analysis the change in length of the beam elements is ignored, bending is therefore the only significant mode on deflection in the system. With this assumption the state variables at the end kk of the kth bay are

$$\mathbf{z}_{kk}^{Rb} = \{ v_{kk} \quad u_{kk,r} \quad \beta_{kk,l} \quad \beta_{kk,r} \quad M_{kk,l} \quad M_{kk,r} \quad Q_{kk} \quad 1 \} \qquad (4.61)$$

Following equation (4.59) the state variables at the end $kk + 1$ are given by

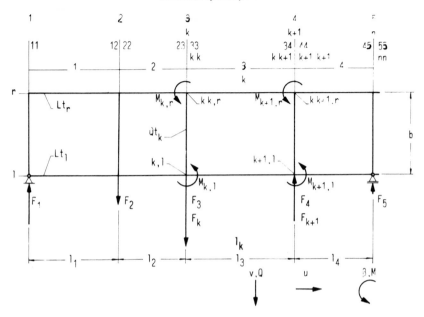

Fig. 4.8 Notation for the analysis of chassis frames in horizontal bending. l – left, r – right hand longitudinal member

$$\mathbf{z}_{kk+1}^{Rb} = \mathbf{F}_k^{Rb} \mathbf{z}_{kk}^{Rb*} \tag{4.62}$$

The transfer matrix $\mathbf{F}_k^{Rb}$ linking the state variables at the two ends of the bay and including the effects of the two side members is shown overleaf.

The elements in this matrix can be obtained from the transfer matrix for the single bay, remembering that there are two parallel beams (side members) transferring the loads. Only the sum of the lateral loads at each cross member are known. They are only equal at each end of the cross member when the side members are the same, but unequal side members do occur, as in the subframes of buses, so that to keep the calculation general the lateral loads are eliminated from the variables by using the lateral displacement v_{kk+1}. This displacement is found from the state variables at end kk from the first row of equation (4.62). In the transfer matrix $\mathbf{F}_k^{Rb}$ the rows for the slope and bending moment contain the terms to be multiplied by v_{kk+1}.

$$\mathbf{z}^{Rb}_{k,k+1} = \begin{Bmatrix} v_{k,k+1} \\ u_{k,k+1,r} \\ \beta_{k,k+1,l} \\ \beta_{k,k+1,r} \\ M_{k,k+1,l} \\ M_{k,k+1,r} \\ Q_{k,k+1} \\ 1 \end{Bmatrix} = $$

	$\{v_{k,k}$	$u_{k,k,r}$	$\beta_{k,k,l}$	$\beta_{k,k,r}$	$M_{k,k,l}$	$M_{k,k,r}$	$Q_{k,k}$	1	$v_{k,k+1}\}$	
	1	0	$-l_k\dfrac{J_{k,l}}{\Sigma J_k}$	$-l_k\dfrac{J_{k,r}}{\Sigma J_k}$	$\dfrac{l_k^2}{2E\Sigma J_k}$	$\dfrac{l_k^2}{2E\Sigma J_k}$	$\dfrac{l_k^3}{6E\Sigma J_k}$	0	0	$\Big\} \, \mathbf{z}^{Rb^r}_{k,k}$
	0	1	0	0	0	0	0	0	0	
	$\dfrac{3}{l_k}$	0	-2	0	$\dfrac{l_k}{2EJ_{k,l}}$	0	0	0	$-\dfrac{3}{l_k}$	
	$\dfrac{3}{l_k}$	0	0	-2	0	$\dfrac{l_k}{2EJ_{k,r}}$	0	0	$-\dfrac{3}{l_k}$	
	$-6\dfrac{EJ_{k,l}}{l_k^2}$	0	$6\dfrac{EJ_{k,l}}{l_k}$	0	-2	0	0	0	$6\dfrac{EJ_{k,l}}{l_k^2}$	
	$-6\dfrac{EJ_{k,r}}{l_k^2}$	0	0	$6\dfrac{EJ_{k,r}}{l_k^2}$	0	-2	0	0	$6\dfrac{EJ_{k,r}}{l_k^2}$	
	0	0	0	0	0	0	1	0	0	
	0	0	0	0	0	0	0	1	0	$\mathbf{F}^{Rb}_k$

where $\Sigma J_k = J_{k,l} + J_{k,r}$

(4.62a)

Along the boundary $k + 1$ the load in the cross member Qt_{k+1} introduces internal loads, which, together with the external load at this section, combine to give the state variables at the front end of the next bay $k + 1$ $k + 1$ as in the equation

$$\mathbf{z}^{Rb}_{k+1 \ k+1} = \mathbf{U}^{Rb}_{k+1} \mathbf{z}^{Rb}_{k \ k+1} \tag{4.63}$$

where the matrix $\mathbf{U}_{k+1}$ is defined here as the nodal transfer matrix. The displacements at the rear of the kth bay are equal to those at the front on the $k + 1$th bay, so that

$$\begin{aligned}
v_{k+1 \ k+1} &= v_{k \ k+1} \\
u_{k+1 \ k+1,r} &= u_{k \ k+1,r} \\
\beta_{k+1 \ k+1,l} &= \beta_{k \ k+1,l} \\
\beta_{k+1 \ k+1,r} &= \beta_{k \ k+1,r}
\end{aligned} \tag{4.64}$$

similarly the loads are transferred across the boundary and the main diagonal of (4.63) consists of 'ones', as shown in

$$
\begin{bmatrix}
v_{k+1 \ k+1} \\
u_{k+1 \ k+1,r} \\
\beta_{k+1 \ k+1,l} \\
\beta_{k+1 \ k+1,r} \\
M_{k+1 \ k+1,l} \\
M_{k+1 \ k+1,r} \\
Q_{k+1 \ k+1} \\
1
\end{bmatrix}
=
\begin{bmatrix}
1 & 0 & 0 & 0 & 0 & 0 & 0 & 0 \\
0 & 1 & 0 & 0 & 0 & 0 & 0 & 0 \\
0 & 0 & 1 & 0 & 0 & 0 & 0 & 0 \\
0 & 0 & 0 & 1 & 0 & 0 & 0 & 0 \\
0 & & & & 1 & 0 & 0 & M_{k+1,l} \\
0 & & C_{k+1} & & 0 & 1 & 0 & M_{k+1,r} \\
0 & 0 & 0 & 0 & 0 & 0 & 1 & F_{k+1} \\
0 & 0 & 0 & 0 & 0 & 0 & 0 & 1
\end{bmatrix}
\begin{bmatrix}
v_{k \ k+1} \\
u_{k \ k+1,r} \\
\beta_{k \ k+1,l} \\
\beta_{k \ k+1,r} \\
M_{k \ k+1,l} \\
M_{k \ k+1,r} \\
Q_{k \ k+1} \\
1
\end{bmatrix}
$$

$$\tag{4.63a}$$

The cross member Qt_{k+1} is deformed by the displacements

$$u_{kk+1,r} \quad \beta_{kk+1,l} \quad \beta_{kk+1,r}$$

The moments at the ends of the cross member result from the load–displacement relations of the cross member considered as a beam element in bending. These relations are combined in the coupling matrix $\mathbf{C}_{k+1}^{Rb}$ which can be written as

$$
\begin{bmatrix} M_{k+1\ k+1,l} \\ \\ M_{k+1\ k+1,r} \end{bmatrix} = \mathbf{C}_{k+1}^{Rb} \begin{bmatrix} u_{k\ k+1,r} \\ \beta_{k\ k+1,l} \\ \beta_{k\ k+1,r} \end{bmatrix}
\tag{4.65}
$$

where

$$
\mathbf{C}_{k+1}^{Rb} = EJ_{Q\ k+1} \begin{bmatrix} -\dfrac{6}{b^2} & -\dfrac{4}{b} & -\dfrac{2}{b} \\ \\ -\dfrac{6}{b^2} & -\dfrac{2}{b} & -\dfrac{4}{b} \end{bmatrix}
\tag{4.66}
$$

This matrix is inserted in the nodal transfer matrix $\mathbf{U}_{k+1}$ in the position indicated in equation (4.63a). The last column of $\mathbf{U}_{k+1}$ contains the external loads, which are usually lateral loads, but, as will be shown, can also be moments acting in the plane of the frame.

The state variables at the front end of bay $k + 1$ can be written in terms of those at the front of bay k by using equations (4.62) and (4.63) in the form

$$
\mathbf{z}_{k+1\ k+1}^{Rb} = \mathbf{u}_{k+1}^{Rb}\mathbf{F}_{k}^{Rb}\mathbf{z}_{kk}^{Rb*}
\tag{4.67}
$$

With this equation the state variables at the rear end of the frame in Fig. 4.8 (end 55) can be calculated from those at the front (end 11). In general, the rear end of the frame will be denoted by the section nn. Examination of Fig. 4.8 shows that negligible elongation is assumed for the side members at the rear end of the frame. This assumption has no effect on the variables at the interior of the frame but gives the boundary conditions at the rear end shown later in equations (4.70)–(4.72). Out of the state variables in equations (4.61) at the front end of the frame the known variables are

$$
v_{11} = 0
\tag{4.68}
$$

$$
Q_{11} = F_1
\tag{4.69}
$$

The unknowns are $u_{11,r}$, $\beta_{11,l}$, $\beta_{11,r}$ and the bending moments $M_{11,l}$ and

$M_{11,r}$. These are connected to the three unknown displacements by the coupling matrix (4.66). At the rear end there are three known conditions

$$v_{nn} = 0 \qquad (4.70)$$

$$M_{nn,l} = 0 \qquad (4.71)$$

$$M_{nn,r} = 0 \qquad (4.72)$$

For practical calculations it is convenient to split the column matrix z_{11}^{Rb} into the sum of column matrices with the unknown variables as coefficients, and a separate column matrix of the external loads at the front end of the frame, as in equation (4.73)

$$
z_{11}^{Rb} = \begin{bmatrix} v_{11} \\ u_{11,r} \\ \beta_{11,l} \\ \beta_{11,r} \\ M_{11,l} \\ M_{11,r} \\ Q_{11} \\ 1 \end{bmatrix} = \begin{bmatrix} 0 \\ 1 \\ 0 \\ 0 \\ -\dfrac{6}{b^2} EJ_{Ql} \\ -\dfrac{6}{b^2} EJ_{Ql} \\ 0 \\ 0 \end{bmatrix} u_{11,r} + \begin{bmatrix} 0 \\ 0 \\ 1 \\ 0 \\ -\dfrac{4}{b} EJ_{Ql} \\ -\dfrac{2}{b} EJ_{Ql} \\ 0 \\ 0 \end{bmatrix} \beta_{11,l} + \begin{bmatrix} 0 \\ 0 \\ 0 \\ 1 \\ -\dfrac{2}{b} EJ_{Ql} \\ -\dfrac{4}{b} EJ_{Ql} \\ 0 \\ 0 \end{bmatrix} \beta_{11,r} + \begin{bmatrix} 0 \\ 0 \\ 0 \\ 0 \\ M_{1,l} \\ M_{1,r} \\ F_1 \\ 1 \end{bmatrix} \qquad (4.73)
$$

This relation can be summarized as

$$z_{11}^{Rb} = z_{11}^{(2)} u_{11,r} + z_{11}^{(3)} \beta_{11,l} + z_{11}^{(4)} \beta_{11,r} + z_{11}^{(8)} \qquad (4.73a)$$

where the superscripts in brackets refer to the row number in the matrices of the state variable. Using equation (4.67) repeatedly on each term until the end nn is reached, the last equation will be

$$z_{nn}^{Rb} = z_{nn}^{(2)} u_{11,r} + z_{nn}^{(3)} \beta_{11,l} + z_{nn}^{(4)} \beta_{11,r} + z_{nn}^{(8)} \qquad (4.74)$$

From the conditions at the rear end summarized in equations (4.70)–(4.72), the 1st, 5th, and 6th terms of matrix z_{nn}^{Rb} are zero, so that

$$v_{nn} = v_{nn}^{(2)} u_{11,r} + v_{nn}^{(3)} \beta_{11,r} + v_{nn}^{(4)} \beta_{11,r} + v_{nn}^{(8)} = 0 \qquad (4.75a)$$

$$M_{nn,l} = M_{nn,l}^{(2)} u_{11,r} + M_{nn,l}^{(3)} \beta_{11,l} + M_{nn,l}^{(4)} \beta_{11,r} + M_{nn,l}^{(8)} = 0 \qquad (4.75b)$$

$$M_{nn,l} = M_{nn,r}^{(2)} u_{11,r} + M_{nn,r}^{(3)} \beta_{11,l} + M_{nn,r}^{(4)} \beta_{11,r} + M_{nn,r}^{(8)} = 0 \qquad (4.75c)$$

where $v_{nn}^{(2)}$ is the first term in the column matrix $z_{nn}^{(2)}$, etc. The unknowns $u_{11,r}, \beta_{11,l}, \beta_{11,r}$ follow from equations (4.75). The bending moments in the front cross member can now be found from these displacements by using the coupling equation (4.65), as in

$$\begin{bmatrix} M_{11,l} \\ \\ M_{11,r} \end{bmatrix} = C_1^{Rb} \begin{bmatrix} u_{11,r} \\ \beta_{11,l} \\ \beta_{11,r} \end{bmatrix} \tag{4.76}$$

Therefore, all the variables are known for the front cross member, and, using equation (4.67) they can be found for all the bay ends and thus for all the ends of the beam elements.

The chassis frame type of structure shown in Fig. 4.8 has, as external loads, both lateral loads and in-plane moments at the nodes. These moments hardly ever occur in practice but they do, however, make it possible to calculate approximately the effect of longitudinal loads on one side of the frame. Since the changes in length of the side members can be neglected in the analysis, the longitudinal external loads can be introduced at any section along the length of the frame. Therefore, they can be introduced as a load system at the rear cross member as illustrated in Fig. 4.9(a). This load system is equivalent to the sum of the systems shown in Fig. 4.9(b) and (c). The system in Fig. 4.9(b) can be analysed by the use of transfer matrices. The bending moment distribution shown in Fig. 4.9(c) is a better approximation to the true distribution when the rear cross member is stiff compared with the other cross members and the side members.

Torsion in a symmetrical chassis frame
Torsion is caused by the action of unsymmetrical loads acting normal to the plane of the frame. The analysis is restricted to symmetrical frames which are almost universally used as vehicle chassis frames. Figure 4.10 shows a frame with 4 cross members with both the general and particular notation used in the analysis. It will be noted that, due to symmetry, it is only necessary to analyse half the frame. Also from symmetry, the bending moments are zero at the centre of the cross members, which, however, carry a constant torque so that the conditions at these points can be represented by longitudinal hinges. Transfer matrices are readily applicable to the side members where the cross members are attached.

The additional displacements (rotations) and loads, shown as the angle

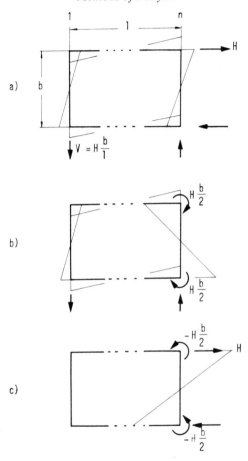

Fig. 4.9 Horizontal bending of a frame by longitudinal loads.
- **(a) External loads**
- **(b) Load system which can be analysed by the method of Fig. 4.8**
- **(c) Load system for a stiff rear cross member which transforms load system (b) into load system (a)**

of twist, φ, and the torque, M_0, in Fig. 4.11 can be added to the state variables at the front end of the kth bay to form the new column matrix

$$\mathbf{z}_{kk}^{Rt} = \{v_{kk} \ \varphi_{kk} \ \beta_{kk} \ M_{kk} \ M_{Dkk} \ Q_{kk} \ 1\} \tag{4.77}$$

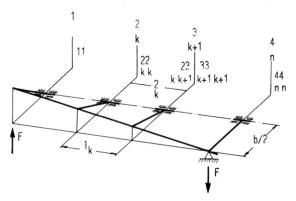

Fig. 4.10   Notation for the analysis of a 4 bay grillage in torsion

The transfer matrix connecting the state variables at the two ends of the bay element is

$$\mathbf{z}_{kk+1}^{Rt} = \mathbf{F}_k^{Rt}\, \mathbf{z}_{kk}^{Rt} \qquad (4.78)$$

This transfer matrix is obtained from the transfer matrix given in equation (4.60) by the addition of the torsional flexibility of the beam in the second

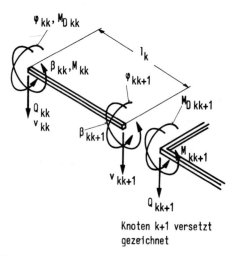

Knoten k+1 versetzt
gezeichnet

Fig. 4.11   State variables at the ends of a beam element in bending and torsion. [Note: node $k + 1$ shown separated]

row (with a negative sign), and a unit in the fifth row corresponding to the torque applied at the end kk. The matrices in equation (4.78) are given in full as

$$
\begin{Bmatrix} v_{kk} & \varphi_{kk} & \beta_{kk} & M_{kk} & M_{Dk\,k} & Q_{kk} & 1 \end{Bmatrix}
$$

$$
\begin{bmatrix} v_{k\,k+1} \\ \varphi_{k\,k+1} \\ \beta_{k\,k+1} \\ M_{k\,k+1} \\ M_{Dk\,k+1} \\ Q_{k\,k+1} \\ 1 \end{bmatrix}
=
\begin{bmatrix}
1 & 0 & -l_k & \dfrac{l_k^2}{2EJ_{Lk}} & 0 & \dfrac{l_k^3}{6EJ_{Lk}} & 0 \\[2ex]
0 & 1 & 0 & 0 & -\dfrac{l_k}{GJ_{tLk}} & 0 & 0 \\[2ex]
0 & 0 & 1 & -\dfrac{l_k}{EJ_{Lk}} & 0 & -\dfrac{l_k^2}{2EJ_{Lk}} & 0 \\[2ex]
0 & 0 & 0 & 1 & 0 & l_k & 0 \\[1ex]
0 & 0 & 0 & 0 & 1 & 0 & 0 \\[1ex]
0 & 0 & 0 & 0 & 0 & 1 & 0 \\[1ex]
0 & 0 & 0 & 0 & 0 & 0 & 1
\end{bmatrix}
\qquad (4.78a)
$$

and the nodal transfer matrix

$$
\mathbf{z}^{Rt}_{k+1\,k+1} = \mathbf{U}^{Rt}_{k+1}\,\mathbf{z}^{Rt}_{kk+1} \qquad (4.79)
$$

follows from the conditions at the $k+1$th cross member which is in bending due to the vertical displacement v_{kk+1} and the angle of twist φ_{kk+1} of the side member at its end. It is also being twisted at its outer end through the angle β_{kk+1}. Equation (4.79) is fully written out in

$$
\begin{Bmatrix} v_{kk+1} & \varphi_{kk+1} & \beta_{kk+1} & M_{kk+1} & M_{Dkk+1} & Q_{kk+1} & 1 \end{Bmatrix}
$$

$$
\begin{bmatrix} v_{k+1\,k+1} \\ \varphi_{k+1\,k+1} \\ \beta_{k+1\,k+1} \\ M_{k+1\,k+1} \\ M_{Dk+1\,k+1} \\ Q_{k+1\,k+1} \\ 1 \end{bmatrix}
=
\begin{bmatrix}
1 & 0 & 0 & 0 & 0 & 0 & 0 \\[1ex]
0 & 1 & 0 & 0 & 0 & 0 & 0 \\[1ex]
0 & 0 & 1 & 0 & 0 & 0 & 0 \\[1ex]
0 & 0 & \left[-\dfrac{2GJ_{t\,Q\,k+1}}{b}\right] & 1 & 0 & 0 & 0 \\[2ex]
\dfrac{12EJ_{Q\,k+1}}{b^2} & -\dfrac{6EJ_{Q\,k+1}}{b} & 0 & 0 & 1 & 0 & 0 \\[2ex]
-\dfrac{24EJ_{Q\,k+1}}{b^3} & \dfrac{12EJ_{Q\,k+1}}{b^2} & 0 & 0 & 0 & 1 & 0 \\[2ex]
0 & 0 & 0 & 0 & 0 & 0 & 1
\end{bmatrix}
$$

$$(4.79a)$$

Equations (4.78) and (4.79) can be combined to give an equation similar to (4.67), which, in generalized form, is

$$\mathbf{z}_{k+1\ k+1} = \mathbf{U}_{k+1}\mathbf{F}_k\mathbf{z}_{kk} \qquad (4.80)$$

Through the continued use of this equation the state variables at the rear cross member can be expressed in terms of those at the front cross member. Assuming, as shown in Fig. 4.10, that there is a support at the rear corner of the frame, i.e. the rear cross member is horizontal, then the state variables at the front are unknown and can be written as

$$v_{11} \ \varphi_{11} \ \beta_{11} \ M_{11} \ M_{D11} \ Q_{11}$$

These are incorporated in the **U** matrix as before. At the section immediately aft of the rear cross member, section *nn* in Fig. 4.10, the zero state variables are

$$v_{nn} = 0 \qquad (4.81a)$$

$$M_{nn} = 0 \qquad (4.81b)$$

$$M_{Dnn} = 0 \qquad (4.81c)$$

from which the state variables at the front cross member can be found. To do this the column matrix $\mathbf{z}_{11}^{Rt}$ is split up into separate terms with the state variables as coefficients, as in equations (4.73)–(4.75).

The above procedure is suitable for the analysis of torsionally stiff frames. In the case of torsionally flexible frames, the torsion constant, J_t, and the second moment of area, J, have such different magnitudes that, after successive multiplication of the transfer matrices, numerical errors can occur. For an approximate analysis of flexible frames this limitation is not essential and can be ignored since the ERZ method described in section 12.1 can be used. Neither this method nor the transfer matrix method so far described involves the analysis of the joint properties of the frame. Therefore both methods give results to the same level of approximation and involve little effort. For frames with open section members the approximation is poor because the effect of the inhibition of warping is not taken into account. For the analysis of stiff frames with closed section members, especially doubly symmetrical warp free sections, the above method is sufficiently accurate.

Bending vibration of a chassis frame
The transfer matrix procedure makes it possible to find the bending natural frequencies and mode shapes of a chassis frame in a simple way.

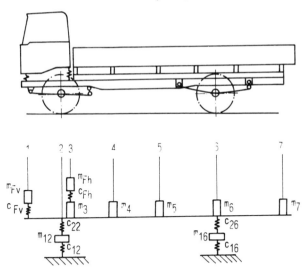

Fig. 4.12 Simplified model used for the analysis of frame bending vibration

The frame shown in Fig. 4.12 is assumed to be massless with its own weight, as well as the remainder of the vehicle weight and the payload, replaced by equivalent lumped masses at nodal points along the frame. The bending stiffness of the load-carrying body is added to the bending stiffness of the chassis over the appropriate length. The internal loads resulting from these assumptions are brought into the analysis through the nodal transfer matrices. Since the cab is normally mounted on flexible mounts it is represented by two lumped masses, each mounted on a separate spring, thus neglecting the mass coupling within the two-degrees-of-freedom sub-system. The frame is supported on mass–spring systems, with the road springs, axle masses, and tyre springs represented separately. Although, in the case of trucks, leaf springs with widely spaced spring hangers are almost universally used, it has been found that it is sufficiently accurate to assume that they act at a single spring support, as shown in Fig. 4.12.

It is an advantage when using transfer matrices to keep the number of effective bays as low as possible. Closely spaced masses or springs can be combined in single nodes having equivalent properties. For instance, in Fig. 4.12 the mass m_{Fh}, representing the rear of the cab, mounted on the spring with a stiffness c_{Fh} is considered to act at the same nodal cross section as the front lumped mass of the load platform, m_3. Comparative calculations have shown that the body cross members in front of and behind the rear axle position can be combined at node 6 without serious error for the first two natural frequencies. It can also be shown that an idealization with approximately 7 nodes gives sufficiently accurate results.

In order to include the effects of the lumped masses and springs in the analysis the dynamic displacements, v, have to be specified as a variable at each node. The load increment at each node is therefore the product of the effective dynamic stiffness and the displacement, which for the rear of bay $k - 1, k$ (node k) can be expressed as

$$\Delta Q = q_k v_{k-1\ k} \qquad (4.82)$$

For oscillations with frequency ω at node k the effective stiffness, q_k, is found as shown in Fig. 4.13. When there are other dynamic effects at the

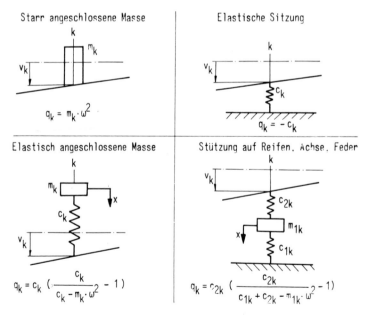

Fig. 4.13   Effective stiffness of different mass/spring combinations at node k.
[Top left, a lumped mass; top right, a simple spring support; bottom left, a spring mass system; bottom right, a suspension system with separate axle mass and tyre spring

same node they can be added to q_k. For example, at node 6 in Fig. 4.12, because of the effects of the mass of the body and payload, as shown above, and of the axle mass, road, and tyre spring, q_s, becomes

$$q_s = m_6\omega^2 + c_{26}\left(\frac{c_{26}}{c_{16} + c_{26} - m_{16}\omega^2} - 1\right)$$

The variables can now be written as

$$\mathbf{z}_{kk} = \{v_{kk} \ \beta_{kk} \ M_{kk} \ Q_{kk}\} \qquad (4.83)$$

The transfer matrix given in equation (4.60) is used, but, as there are no static external loads, the fifth row and column are eliminated. The **U** matrix is now

$$\mathbf{U}_k = \begin{bmatrix} 1 & 0 & 0 & 0 \\ 0 & 1 & 0 & 0 \\ 0 & 0 & 1 & 0 \\ q_k & 0 & 0 & 1 \end{bmatrix} \qquad (4.84)$$

At the front of the frame the displacements v_{11} and β_{11} are unknown. The loads are

$$M_{11} = 0$$
$$Q_{11} = q_1 \ v_{11}$$

Equation (4.83) can be written as in equation (4.73) with the state variables as coefficients

$$\mathbf{z}_{11} = \begin{bmatrix} 1 \\ 0 \\ 0 \\ q_1 \end{bmatrix} v_{11} + \begin{bmatrix}) \\ 1 \\ ) \\ ) \end{bmatrix} \beta_{11} = \mathbf{z}_{11}^{(1)} v_{11} + \mathbf{z}_{11}^{(2)} \beta_{11} \qquad (4.85)$$

At the rear of the frame the load variables beyond the last node n are

$$M_{nn} = 0$$
$$Q_{nn} = 0 \qquad (4.86)$$

so that the third and fourth row terms of $\mathbf{z}_{nn}$ are zero and the equivalent rows of (4.85) become

$$M_{nn} = M_{nn}^{(1)}v_{11} + M_{nn}^{(2)}\beta_{11} = 0$$

$$Q_{nn} = Q_{nn}^{(1)}v_{11} + Q_{nn}^{(2)}\beta_{11} = 0$$

(4.87)

and the unknowns v_{11} and β_{11} can be found.

For non-trivial solutions of this set of homogenous equations the determinant of the coefficients must be zero, therefore

$$M_{nn}^{(1)}Q_{nn}^{(2)} - M_{nn}^{(2)}Q_{nn}^{(1)} = 0 \qquad (4.88)$$

By successive multiplication of the transfer matrices, using the elements containing ω^2 in the nodal transfer matrices, the higher exponents of ω^2 and consequently the higher orders of natural frequencies can be obtained. Equation (4.88) is a polynomial with the same order as the power of ω^2 which cannot be solved explicitly. The recommended method of solution is to calculate the left hand side for values of ω^2 close to the expected value and interpolate to find the zero value of the left hand side. Now that ω^2, $M_{nn}^{(1)}$, $M_{nn}^{(2)}$, $Q_{nn}^{(1)}$ and $Q_{nn}^{(2)}$ are known, there follows from equation (4.87)

$$\frac{v_{11}}{\beta_{11}} = -\frac{M_{nn}^{(2)}}{M_{nn}^{(1)}} = -\frac{Q_{nn}^{(2)}}{Q_{nn}^{(1)}} \qquad (4.89)$$

For a given deflection and associated slope at the front of the frame the displacements at the other nodes can be found from the transfer matrices when the frequencies obtained from equation (4.88) are inserted into the nodal transfer matrices. In this way the mode shapes of the vibrating frame can be found at the natural frequencies calculated.

5

Warping of open-section thin-walled beams

The effects of warping or deplanation of the cross section of thin walled beams can be as important as bending in the determination of the stresses and displacements of these structural elements. In spite of this, the theory is still little known and rather unpopular. One of the main reasons for this is that a well-rounded, comprehensive treatment of the theory has only recently been available. The work of Vlassov (15) or Kollbrunner and Hajdin (8) must be referred to in this connection. These works often appear too general and theoretical for practical application. For this reason a short summary of the theory is given here with an emphasis on the important relationships for the analysis of commercial vehicle chassis frames.

Warping of the cross section of a thin-walled beam occurs mainly in torsion, but it can also arise from longitudinal loads, except when they act through special points on the cross section, and bending moments caused by pairs of normal loads acting in planes which do not pass through the torsion centre. In the case of open-section thin-walled beams, which are dealt with in this chapter, torsional loads are usually associated with the inhibition of warping which occurs at joints between the beams. The direct stresses caused by warping inhibition can be decisive in designing for the durability of chassis frames, and they can only be found from an understanding of the effects of warping at the joints. The theory points to the fact that the torque arising from inhibition of warping is the focal point of interest. Naturally, all the load–displacement characteristics of the beam are involved, e.g., if a beam is subject to warping from longitudinal loads, and if the warping is inhibited, it will carry a torque as well as direct loads. The notation used here is becoming almost universal. [*Editor's Note*. Unfortunately many of the existing published works use different notations depending on the source each author originally used.]

At any cross section of a beam a new internal load system, the bimoment, must be added to the six loads described in chapter 4. The strain energy due to the six internal loads was found by multiplying them by their corresponding displacements so that the bimoment must be

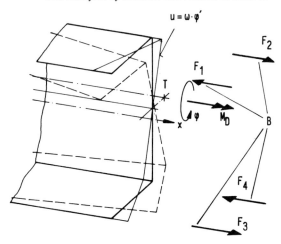

Fig. 5.1   Loads and displacements at the end of an open-section thin-walled beam under torsion

multiplied by its corresponding displacement, which in this case, is the rate of change of twist, i.e., the derivative of the angle of twist with respect to the longitudinal coordinate of the beam φ'. The shortened notation of 'rate of twist' is used for this parameter. To clarify this Fig. 5.1 shows the end of a channel section thin-walled beam twisted about the shear or torsion centre axis which passes through the point T. It is difficult to visualize the warped shape from the deformed cross section, shown dotted, so it is shown separately, superimposed on the original cross section and indicated by the longitudinal displacement, u. The warping can be due to two different load systems, either the torque M_D which twists the beam causing the warping, or the set of longitudinal forces, F_1–F_4, which warp the cross section directly and cause it to twist. The longitudinal loads F_1–F_4 form a self-equilibrating group which is called the Bimoment B acting on the cross section. In this simple form the bimoment is made up from two equal and opposite couples in parallel planes a fixed distance apart. The value of the bimoment is the product of the moment of the couples and the distance apart of the planes. It has the dimensions of force × length squared (Ncm^2). It can also be noted that the product of the bimoment and the rate of twist has the dimension of work (Ncm).

Bimoments can also be defined in terms of a distribution of longitudinal stress over the cross section. This definition is not so easily understood as the one based on four separate forces, although it is the most common form and will be used later. The warping displacement at any point in the cross section is given by the product of the rate of twist φ' and the unit warping, ω, which will be defined later. Since the rate of twist is a constant at any cross section, the warped shape of the cross section depends only on ω, which, in turn, depends only on the profile of the thin walled beam.

The differential equation of twist along a thin-walled beam
There are two main hypotheses in the theory of warping which have been shown by experiment to be sufficient for the analysis of chassis frames

(1) The profile of the cross section is maintained constant.
(2) Shear deformation is neglected.

The relation between the displacement along the tangent to the profile of the section, f, and the longitudinal warping displacement, u, is found by applying the second hypothesis, i.e., the shear strain γ is zero, so that

$$\frac{\partial f}{\partial x} + \frac{\partial u}{\partial s} = 0 \tag{5.1}$$

The coordinates and displacement directions are shown in Fig. 5.2 on the undeformed beam. This example of a torsion cantilever is rigidly fixed at end 1 and has a torque, M_D, applied at end 2. The coordinate, s, and the displacement, f, along the profile are both positive when clockwise about the x axis. Symmetrical open-section thin-walled sections are usually used in the design of chassis frames. The channel section shown as the example in Fig. 5.2 is, therefore, typical of a side member of a truck chassis. This section is chosen also because the displacements and loads can be illustrated a little more clearly than is the case for the arbitrary cross sections usually chosen in general theoretical treatments of the subject. However, there is no loss of validity in the development of the theory. By integrating the kinematic relation of equation (5.1) the warping displacement, u, is

$$u = -\int_0^s \frac{\partial f}{\partial x} \, ds \tag{5.2}$$

The integration constant in equation (5.2) is zero because the warping

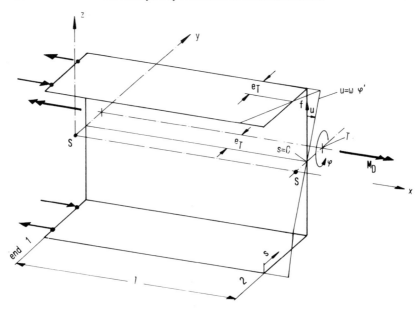

Fig. 5.2   Channel-section thin-walled beam torsion cantilever, warping inhibited at end 1

displacement is symmetrical and s can be taken as zero on the line of symmetry, which, in this case, is the centre of the web.

Since the derivation of the position of the torsion axis or shear centre axis for an open-section thin-walled beam is well known it will not be repeated here.

The tangential displacement, f, of a point on the profile for a rotation φ of the section about the torsion centre, T, is given by

$$f = -r\varphi \qquad (5.3)$$

where r is the distance from the torsion centre, T, to the tangent, as shown in Fig. 5.3. From Fig. 5.2 it can be seen that a positive rotation, φ, which is clockwise about the x axis, results in a negative displacement of the web which is opposite to the positive direction of s; however, the displacement of the flanges is positive. The sign of r depends on this relation and is chosen so that it is positive for the web, i.e., opposite to the sign of the displacement. This sign convention is chosen because the warping dis-

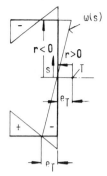

Fig. 5.3 **Sign convention for *r* and unit warping displacement of a channel section**

placement, u, increases as s increases when r is positive, as shown in Fig. 5.2. The sign of r can also be chosen, as in **(15)**, to be positive when the positive s direction is anticlockwise about T when viewed along the positive x direction.

From equations (5.2) and (5.3) the warping displacement u, as a function of s, becomes

$$u(s) = \varphi' \int_0^s r \, \mathrm{d}s \qquad (5.4)$$

Where the integral can be written as

$$\omega(s) = \int_0^s r \, \mathrm{d}s \qquad (5.5)$$

so that

$$u(s) = \omega(s)\varphi' \qquad (5.6)$$

and $\omega(s)$ can be defined as the unit warping displacement of the point s. The point $s = 0$ is also the point where $\omega = 0$.

The distribution of $\omega(s)$ is shown in Fig. 5.3 for a channel section. Figure 5.2 shows the warping distribution of the free end, end 2, of a torsion cantilever where there is no inhibition of warping. The twist per unit length of such a member is positive at the free end for positive twist, i.e., the rate of twist φ' is positive. It will be noticed that there are points of zero warping in the flanges as well as in the web which are the same distance e_T from the web as the torsion centre is from the web.

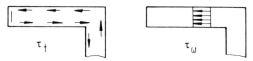

Fig. 5.4   Shear stress distribution through the thickness for St Venant torsion τ_t and for warping stress τ_ω

The deformation of the end of the beam has to be related to the torque acting on the beam at the same cross section. The St Venant torsion is transferred by a shear stress of the type shown in Fig. 5.4 as τ_t, while the shear stress associated with warping is shown as τ_ω.

The shear flow is then

$$q_\omega = t\tau_\omega$$

and the torque is

$$M_\omega = \int_U rq_\omega \, ds \tag{5.7}$$

M_ω is usually due to end conditions which cause inhibition of warping. The relationship between this torque and the direct stress associated with warping inhibition is derived from the equilibrium of the rectangular element shown in Fig. 5.5, which lies in the x–s plane of Fig. 5.2.

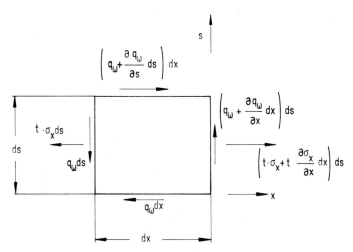

Fig. 5.5   Stress and shear flow distribution on an element of an open-section thin-walled beam

For equilibrium in the x direction

$$\frac{\partial q_\omega}{\partial s} + t\frac{\partial \sigma_x}{\partial x} = 0$$

so that

$$q_\omega = -\int \frac{\partial \sigma_x}{\partial x} t \, ds \tag{5.8}$$

The strain in the x direction follows from equation (5.6) and is

$$\varepsilon_x = \frac{\partial u}{\partial x} = \omega\varphi'' \tag{5.9}$$

so that the stress is

$$\sigma_x = E\omega\varphi'' \tag{5.10}$$

the shear flow then becomes, from (5.8)

$$q_\omega = -E\varphi''' \int_A \omega \, dA \tag{5.11}$$

where A is the actual cross sectional area of the material. From equation (5.7) the warping torque becomes

$$M_\omega = -E\varphi''' \int_A \omega^2 \, dA \tag{5.12}$$

then

$$J_\omega = \int_A \omega^2 \, dA \tag{5.13}$$

where J_ω is a property of the cross section and is called the torsion constant due to warping. Equation (5.12) can now be written as

$$M_\omega = -EJ_\omega\varphi''' \tag{5.14}$$

The equivalent equation for St Venant torsion is well known as

$$M_t = GJ_t\varphi' \tag{5.15}$$

with the St Venant torsion constant

$$J_t = \tfrac{1}{3}\Sigma \, \Delta s t^3 \tag{5.16}$$

The total torque is the sum of the two torques

$$M_D = M_\omega + M_t \qquad (5.17)$$

$$M_D = -EJ_\omega \varphi''' + GJ_t \varphi' \qquad (5.18)$$

When no external torque is introduced along the length of the beam, M_D is also constant, so that the important differential equation for the distribution of twist along the beam becomes

$$EJ_\omega \varphi^{iv} - GJ_t \varphi'' = 0 \qquad (5.19)$$

The bimoment
If the self-equilibrating system of loads causing warping are discrete forces as shown in Fig. 5.1, the bimoment is

$$B = \Sigma_i \, F_i \omega_i \qquad (5.20)$$

where ω_i is the unit warping displacement of the point of application of the force F_i. If the longitudinal loads are continuously distributed, causing a stress distribution σ_x over the cross section, the bimoment is defined as

$$B = \int_A \sigma_x \omega \, dA \qquad (5.21)$$

Several practical relationships result from this. First, from equation (5.10) the bimoment becomes

$$B = EJ_\omega \varphi'' \qquad (5.22)$$

or

$$\sigma_x = \frac{B}{J_\omega} \omega \qquad (5.23)$$

Then, combining equations (5.14) and (5.22) there follows

$$M_\omega = -B' \qquad (5.24)$$

Since shear flow is a more useful quantity than shear stress, equations (5.11) and (5.12) are used to give

$$q_\omega = \frac{M_\omega}{J_\omega} S_\omega \qquad (5.25)$$

where $S_\omega(s)$ is defined by the author as the static warping moment

$$S_\omega(s) = \int_0^s \omega \, dA \qquad (5.26)$$

[*Editor's Note.* There is no generally accepted name for this quantity in the British literature.]

Finally, from equation (5.24), the shear flow becomes

$$q_\omega = \frac{B'}{J_\omega} S_\omega \qquad (5.27)$$

Load displacement relations
The differential equation (5.19) can be written as

$$\varphi^{iv} - \alpha^2 \varphi'' = 0 \qquad (5.28)$$

where

$$\alpha^2 = \frac{GJ_t}{EJ_\omega} \qquad (5.29)$$

The solution can be written in the form

$$\varphi = C_1 \cosh \alpha x + C_2 \sinh \alpha x + C_3 x + C_4$$

At $x = 0$, φ and its derivatives become

$$\varphi_0 = C_1 + C_4 \qquad (a)$$
$$\varphi_0' = \alpha C_2 + C_3 \qquad (b)$$
$$\varphi_0'' = \alpha^2 C_1 \qquad (c)$$
$$\varphi_0''' = \alpha^3 C_2 \qquad (d)$$

The constants can be obtained as follows, from equation (5.22) and (c) above

$$C_1 = \frac{1}{\alpha^2} \frac{B_0}{EJ_\omega}$$

from equation (5.18) and (d)

$$C_2 = \frac{-M_D - GJ_t \varphi_0'}{EJ_\omega \alpha^3}$$

then from (a)

$$C_4 = \varphi_0 - \frac{1}{\alpha^2} \frac{B_0}{EJ_\omega}$$

and from (b)

$$C_3 = \frac{M_D - GJ_t\varphi_0'}{EJ_\omega\alpha^2} + \varphi_0'$$

The internal loads and displacements at any point x along a beam can now be found. These are given as a set of coefficients of the variables at $x = 0$, i.e., φ_0, φ_0', B_0, and M_D, with the St Venant torsional stiffness of the beam defined as

$$\eta = GJ_t \tag{5.30}$$

The coefficients in the equations in tabular form

	φ_0	φ_0'	B_0	M_D	
$\varphi(x) =$	1	$\dfrac{1}{\alpha}\sinh\alpha x$	$\dfrac{1}{\eta}(\cosh\alpha x - 1)$	$\dfrac{1}{\eta}\left(x - \dfrac{1}{\alpha}\sinh\alpha x\right)$	(5.31a)
$\varphi'(x) =$		$\cosh\alpha x$	$\dfrac{\alpha}{\eta}\sinh\alpha x$	$\dfrac{1}{\eta}(1 - \cosh\alpha x)$	(5.31b)
$B(x) =$		$\dfrac{\eta}{\alpha}\sinh\alpha x$	$\cosh\alpha x$	$-\dfrac{1}{\alpha}\sinh\alpha x$	(5.31c)
$M_D(x) =$				1	

These equations give the load–displacement relations at the ends of the beam which can be combined in the matrix equation

$$\begin{bmatrix} \varphi \\ \varphi_1' \\ \varphi_2' \end{bmatrix} = \frac{1}{\eta}\begin{bmatrix} l & 1 & 1 \\ 1 & \alpha\coth\alpha l & \dfrac{\alpha}{\sinh\alpha l} \\ 1 & \dfrac{\alpha}{\sinh\alpha l} & \alpha\coth\alpha l \end{bmatrix}\begin{bmatrix} M_D \\ B_1 \\ B_2 \end{bmatrix} \tag{5.32}$$

The positive load and displacement directions are shown in Fig. 5.6 with four discrete forces used to indicate the bimoment. This figure, together with Fig. 5.2, shows that the sign convention used means that a positive bimoment causes positive warping and, therefore, positive rate of twist.

Since there is no external torque applied along the beam element the internal torque is the same at all points along its length, therefore

$$M_D = M_{D2} = -M_{D1} \tag{5.33}$$

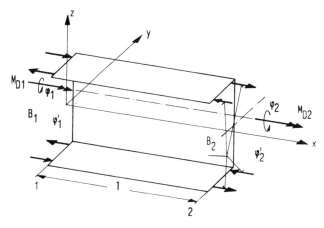

Fig. 5.6 **Sign convention for loads and displacements in a warped channel-section beam element**

At this point the reader should be reminded of the difference between the internal loads (due to imaginary cuts) and the loads acting on the ends of the beam element. From Figs 5.6 and 5.2, a positive bimoment at end 2 causes positive internal direct stresses, σ, where the unit warping, ω, is positive. Equation (5.21) shows that if both σ and ω are positive, then the internal bimoment B is also positive, whereas a positive external bimoment acting on end 1 results in a negative internal bimoment.

Bimoments due to discrete loads
It was stated at the beginning of the chapter that discrete longitudinal loads acting on thin-walled beams cause warping. According to equation (5.20) a bimoment occurs when longitudinal loads are applied at any point where the unit warping is not zero. If equal discrete longitudinal loads are applied in the same direction to points of equal values of ω which have opposite signs, the bimoments will cancel out. An example of this would be equal loads applied to the intersections of the web and flanges of a channel section. Warping can also be induced by two equal and opposite forces acting laterally on the beam. Figure 5.7 shows an example where the forces are F_Q, separated by a distance, a, and act in a plane parallel to the torsion axis and at a distance, e, from it. The forces are equivalent to a pair of forces $F_Q a/b$ acting at the edges of the flange, as shown in

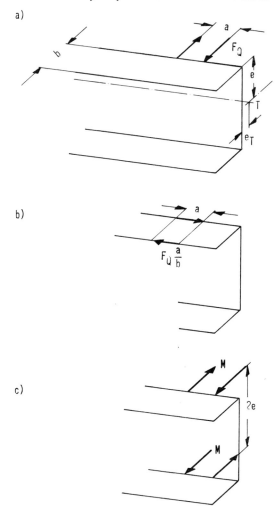

Fig. 5.7   Couples that introduce a bimoment into a channel section

Fig. 5.7(b). These forces cause a bimoment as in equation (5.20) with the value of ω given in equation (5.5), i.e.

$$B = F_Q \frac{a}{b} e_T e - F_Q \frac{a}{b} (e_T e - eb) = F_Q ae$$

This example shows that a bending moment, M, made up from equal and opposite lateral forces acting in a plane which is a distance, e, from the torsion centre results in a bimoment

$$B = Me \qquad (5.34)$$

If the bimoment is considered as two opposite bending moments separated by a distance, as shown in Figs 5.1 and 5.6, it becomes clear from Fig. 5.7(c) that in this case the bimoment is $B = 2Me$. This is important for the transfer of bimoments across the joints of chassis frames. The compatibility of the corresponding displacements is dealt with in chapter 8.

6
Closed-section thin-walled beams in torsion

The effect of warping in closed-section thin-walled beams is much less important than in open sections. In particular the inhibition of warping does not generally produce large torques. For the stress analysis of vehicle frames with closed section cross members, however, the compatibility of any warping displacement in the cross member and rate of twist in the side member has to be ensured at the joints. Even when warp-free sections are used, e.g., circular or square sections, any non-zero twisting strain of the beam to which they are joined at a node has to be taken into account. The assumptions made for open sections – that the cross-section shape remains constant and that there is negligible shear deformation – do not hold for closed sections as they lead to kinematically impossible deformations. The additional displacements arising from the deformation of the cross section can be added to the displacements assumed for open sections and a so-called lateral bimoment added to the internal loads.

The load–displacement relations for torsion in closed sections are derived for rectangular box beams, as they are the most common sections used in practice. These relations are more complex than those developed for open sections and, although derived for box beams, they are actually a special case of the general relationships applying to all closed sections.

Deformation of box beams in torsion
Figure 6.1 shows the positive directions of the beam coordinates, x, y, z, and s, the coordinate taken round the profile of the section. It also indicates the positive directions of the displacements of a point on the periphery of the section, u, out of the plane of the section, and, f, in the tangential direction in the plane of the section. The u displacements represent warping, while the f displacements represent both rotation and lozenging of the cross section. Both displacements are functions of the longitudinal and tangential coordinates and can be written $u(s, x)$ and $f(s, x)$. As in the case of open sections, they are assumed to be linear functions of s. The total deformation can be separated into three parts, as shown in Fig. 6.2. Each can again be divided into two parts, the shape

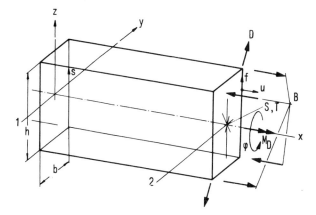

Fig. 6.1   Sign convention for loads and displacements of a box beam element in torsion

function depending on s, and the magnitude depending on x, the distance along the beam.

The warping displacement of any point can therefore be written as the product of two functions

$$u = \chi(s)W(x) \qquad (6.1)$$

In the case of a rectangular box beam the zero warping points are at the centres of the sides, see Fig. 6.2, so that the warping function can be

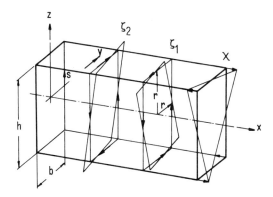

Fig. 6.2   Displacement functions of a box beam

written as

$$\chi(s) = y(s)z(s) \tag{6.2}$$

The displacements in the plane of the cross section are displacements of the sides of the rectangle in the direction of the coordinate s. Since the length of the sides remain constant, the resulting shape is a parallelogram. The opposite sides of the rectangle are therefore displaced an equal and opposite amount in proportion to their distance, r, from the centre. The possible displaced shape can then be shown to be the sum of two displacements: a pure rotation and a pure lozenging. The associated displacement functions are defined as ζ_1 and ζ_2 and are shown in Fig. 6.2.

The total in plane displacement becomes

$$f = \zeta_1(s)V_1(x) + \zeta_2(s)V_2(x) \tag{6.3}$$

where

$$\zeta_1(s) = r(s) \tag{6.4}$$

$$\zeta_2(s) = y'(s)z(s) + y(s)z'(s) \tag{6.5}$$

In the case of the upper horizontal side of the rectangular cross section, for example, the functions have the values: $y'(s) = -1$, $z(s) = h/2$, $z'(s) = 0, \xi = -h/2$, and the displacement is in the negative s direction.

Differential equation of deformation along the beam
Both the longitudinal stress, σ_x, and the shear stress, τ, will vary along the length of the element of the rectangular thin-walled beam shown in Fig. 6.3. The equilibrium conditions for the two ends of the elemental strip can be found by using the method of virtual displacements, where the total work done in each virtual displacement is zero. A virtual displacement in the x direction is given directly by equation (6.1) as

$$\delta u = \chi(s)\delta W \tag{6.6}$$

From Fig. 6.3 the external force in the x direction acting on the element must be

$$\frac{\partial \sigma}{\partial x} \, dx \, dA \tag{6.7}$$

where dA is an element of the cross sectional area of the material in the beam.

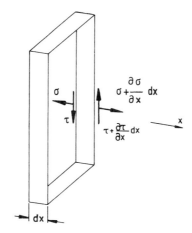

Fig. 6.3 Elemental strip of a box beam

The internal displacements compatible with the external virtual displacements are the increments of shear strain

$$\delta\gamma = \frac{\partial\chi}{\partial s}\,\delta W$$

and the shear stresses, τ, are the corresponding internal forces. The length of the strip, dx, is assumed constant so that the direct strains are zero and the total virtual work done over the material cross section, A, by the direct loads, and over the volume of material, V, by the shear loads, must be zero, so that

$$\int_A \frac{\partial\sigma}{\partial x}\,dx\chi(s)\delta W\,dA - \int_V \tau\,\frac{\partial\chi}{\partial s}\,\delta W\,dV = 0 \qquad (6.8)$$

where $dV = dx\,dA$. Since dx and δW are independent of the position on the periphery of the cross section they can be taken out of the integrals, so that the equilibrium condition for the forces in the longitudinal direction is

$$\int_A \frac{\partial\sigma}{\partial x}\,\chi(s)\,dA - \int_A \tau\,\frac{\partial\chi}{\partial s}\,dA = 0 \qquad (6.9)$$

For equilibrium in the tangential direction virtual displacements corresponding to the two displacement functions in equation (6.3) have to be made, see reference **(4)**, leading to

$$\int_A \frac{\partial \tau}{\partial x} \zeta_1 \, dA = 0 \tag{6.10}$$

$$\int_A \frac{\partial \tau}{\partial x} \zeta_2 \, dA - 8 \frac{Et^3}{b+h} V_2 = 0 \tag{6.11}$$

The compatibility of the strains and displacements must be maintained so that

$$\varepsilon_x = \frac{\partial u}{\partial x} \tag{6.12}$$

$$\gamma_{sx} = \frac{\partial u}{\partial s} + \frac{\partial f}{\partial x} \tag{6.13}$$

The usual stress–strain relations also apply, i.e.

$$\sigma = E\varepsilon_x \tag{6.14}$$

$$\tau = G\gamma_{sx} \tag{6.15}$$

Using the displacement functions for u and f from equations (6.1) and (6.3), equations (6.14) and (6.12) become

$$\sigma = E \frac{\partial u}{\partial x} = E\chi(s) \frac{\partial W}{\partial x} \tag{6.16}$$

also equations (6.15) and (6.13) become

$$\tau = G\left\{ \frac{\partial u}{\partial s} + \frac{\partial f}{\partial x} \right\}$$
$$= G\left\{ \frac{\partial \chi}{\partial s} W(x) + \zeta_1(s) \frac{\partial V_1}{\partial x} + \zeta_2(s) \frac{\partial V_2}{\partial x} \right\} \tag{6.17}$$

Substituting in equation (6.9), the warping or longitudinal displacement relation becomes

$$E \int_A \chi^2(s) \frac{\partial^2 W}{\partial x^2} \, dA - G\left\{ \int_A \left(\frac{\partial \chi}{\partial s} \right)^2 W(x) \, dA \right.$$
$$\left. + \int_A \zeta_1(s) \frac{\partial V_1}{\partial x} \frac{\partial \chi}{\partial s} \, dA + \int_A \zeta_2(s) \frac{\partial V_2}{\partial x} \frac{\partial \chi}{\partial s} \, dA \right\} = 0 \tag{6.18}$$

Closed-section thin-walled beams in torsion

59

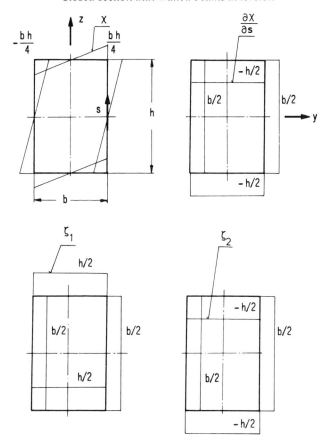

Fig. 6.4 Displacement functions in the plane of the cross section of a box beam. (Note. Positive values of the functions are shown to the right of the cross section outline when viewed in the positive direction of s.)

The terms not dependent on s can again be taken out of the integrals. The remaining integrals, which depend only on the dimensions of the cross section, as shown in Fig. 6.4, can be integrated in turn to give the coefficients

$$\int_A \chi^2 \, \mathrm{d}A = \frac{t}{24} b^2 h^2 (b + h) = a_1 \qquad (6.19\mathrm{a})$$

$$\int_A \left(\frac{\partial \chi}{\partial s}\right)^2 dA = \frac{t}{2} bh(b + h) = a_2 \qquad (6.19\text{b})$$

$$\int_A \zeta_1 \frac{\partial \chi}{\partial s} dA = \frac{t}{2} bh(b - h) = a_3 \qquad (6.19\text{c})$$

$$\int_A \zeta_2 \frac{\partial \chi}{\partial s} dA = \frac{t}{2} bh(b + h) = a_2 \qquad (6.19\text{d})$$

For rotation of the cross section, equations (6.10) and (6.17) give

$$G\left\{\int_A \frac{\partial \chi}{\partial s} \frac{\partial W}{\partial x} \zeta_1 dA + \int_A \zeta_1^2 \frac{\partial^2 V_1}{\partial x^2} dA + \int_A \zeta_1\zeta_2 \frac{\partial^2 V_2}{\partial x^2} dA\right\} = 0$$

$$(6.20)$$

From Fig. 6.4 it can be seen that ζ_2 has the same distribution as $\partial\chi/\partial s$ so that

$$\int_A \zeta_1\zeta_2 dA = a_3 \qquad (6.19\text{e})$$

and again from Fig. 6.4 $(\partial\chi/\partial s)^2 = \zeta_1^2$, so that

$$\int_A \zeta_1^2 dA = a_2 \qquad (6.19\text{f})$$

For lozenging of the section equations (6.11) and (6.17) give

$$G\left\{\int_A \frac{\partial \chi}{\partial s} \frac{\partial W}{\partial x} \zeta_2 dA + \int_A \zeta_1\zeta_2 \frac{\partial^2 V_1}{\partial x^2} dA + \int_A \zeta_2^2 \frac{\partial^2 V_2}{\partial x^2} dA\right\}$$
$$- 8 \frac{Et^3}{b + h} V_2 = 0 \qquad (6.21)$$

but $\zeta_2 = \partial\chi/\partial s$, so that

$$\int_A \zeta_2^2 dA = a_2 \qquad (6.19\text{g})$$

A further coefficient occurring in the equations and which only depends on the dimensions of the cross section is

$$\frac{8t^3}{b + h} = a_4 \qquad (6.19\text{h})$$

The system of differential equations (6.18), (6.20) and (6.21) can now be written with the coefficients defined in (6.19) as

$$a_1 E W'' - a_2 G W - a_3 G V_1' - a_2 G V_2' = 0 \qquad (6.22a)$$

$$a_3 W' + a_2 V_1'' + a_3 V_2'' = 0 \qquad (6.22b)$$

$$a_2 G W' + a_3 G V_1'' + a_2 G V_2'' - a_4 E V_2 = 0 \qquad (6.22c)$$

Generalized displacements and internal loads

The displacement functions defined in equations (6.2), (6.4), and (6.5) can be regarded as generalized coordinates. The corresponding generalized displacements W, V_1, and V_2 define the magnitude of each of the three generalized coordinates making up the total displacement of the cross section at any location. This can be seen most clearly in the case of rotation where the generalized displacement, V_1, is the angle of twist, φ.

Generalized forces can be defined corresponding to the generalized displacements. For twist, the corresponding force is simply the torque, M_D, which produces the rotation, φ. The other two generalized forces are the bimoment, B, and the lateral bimoment, D, which will be explained in more detail later. The relation between the internal loads and the stresses in the cross section can be found by considering the virtual work done by the generalized forces moving through the virtual generalized displacements and equating this work with that of the stresses moving through the displacements of the points where they are acting.

In the case of rotation, the virtual generalized displacement, $\delta\varphi = \delta V_1$. The in-plane displacement equation (6.3) has a term corresponding to rotation which, for a virtual displacement can be written as

$$\delta f_1 = \zeta_1(s) \delta V_1 \qquad (6.23)$$

so that the virtual work equation becomes

$$M_D \delta\varphi = \int_A \tau \delta f_1 \, dA = \int_V \tau \zeta_1 \delta\varphi \, dA \qquad (6.24)$$

$\delta\varphi$ is independent of the coordinate s, so that it can be taken out of the integral, and ζ_1 is defined in equation (6.4), and equation (6.24) gives the well known results

$$M_D = \int_A \tau r \, dA \qquad (6.25)$$

which could equally well be obtained from first principles.

In the case of warping, the virtual displacement is given by equation

(6.6) and the bimoment is the corresponding force system, so that

$$B\delta W = \int_A \sigma\delta u \, \mathrm{d}A = \int_A \sigma\chi\delta W \, \mathrm{d}A \qquad (6.26)$$

Since W is again independent of s, the bimoment is

$$B = \int_A \sigma\chi \, \mathrm{d}A \qquad (6.27)$$

The lozenging generalized displacement is associated with the lateral bimoment, D. This is a set of self-equilibrating shear forces which are shown in Fig. 6.5 as the product of the shear stress, τ, the length of the sides, and the thickness of the material, t. This must not be confused with the longitudinal bimoment, B, consisting of a self-equilibrating set of longitudinal forces, which will be referred to simply as the bimoment. The virtual displacement corresponding to the lateral bimoment is δV_2 and from the lozenging term in equation (6.3) the in-plane displacement is

$$\delta f_2 = \zeta_2(s)\delta V_2 \qquad (6.28)$$

and the virtual work equation is

$$D\delta V_2 = \int_A \tau\delta f_2 \, \mathrm{d}A = \int_A \tau\zeta_2\delta V_2 \, \mathrm{d}A \qquad (6.29)$$

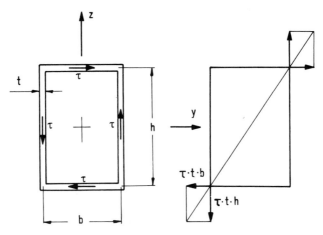

Fig. 6.5   Shear stress due to the lateral bimoment

Again the displacement function, V_2, is independent of s, so that

$$D = \int_A \tau \zeta_2 \, dA \qquad (6.30)$$

From equations (6.25), (6.27), and (6.30), and using equations (6.16) and (6.17), the internal loads at any cross section can be written in terms of the generalized warping displacement W, the twist, φ (rather than V_1), and the generalized lozenging displacement, V (used in place of V_2), as

$$M_D = G(a_3 W + a_2 \varphi' + a_3 V') \qquad (6.31a)$$

$$B = E a_1 W' \qquad (6.31b)$$

$$D = G(a_2 W + a_3 \varphi' + a_2 V') \qquad (6.31c)$$

The coefficients are obtained from equations (6.19).

Load–displacement relations
Using the physical definitions of the generalized displacements given above, equations (6.22) can be written

$$a_1 E W'' - a_2 G W - a_3 G \varphi' - a_2 G V' = 0 \qquad (6.32a)$$

$$a_3 W' + a_2 \varphi'' + a_3 V'' = 0 \qquad (6.32b)$$

$$a_2 G W' + a_3 G \varphi'' + a_2 G V'' - a_4 E V = 0 \qquad (6.32c)$$

A solution of this set of equations is given in references (4) and (15) where the relations between state variables $\varphi(x)$, $W(x)$, $V(x)$, $M_D(x)$, $B(x)$, $D(x)$ at any point x along the beam are also given when the beam has the state variables, φ_0, W_0, V_0, M_{D0}, B_0, D_0 at the end 1. These expressions are considerably more complicated than the corresponding expressions for open-section thin-walled beams given in equation (5.31), and it has been decided not to reproduce them here. The flexibility matrices obtained from the results are given in chapter 12.2.1, and they can be seen in more detail in reference (4). For practical purposes it is normally possible to neglect the lozenging effects and a simplified method based on this approximation will be presented in the following section.

Figure 6.6 shows the distribution of the bimoment, lateral bimoment, warping, and lozenging functions for two rectangular and two square sections with equal total length of sides and different thicknesses subjected to equal bimoments at each end with lozenging inhibited at the ends. These conditions correspond to those at the ends of cross members.

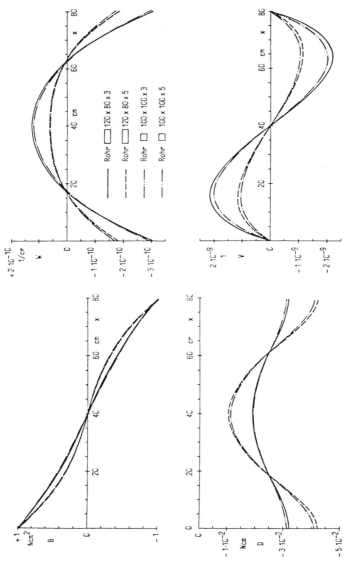

Fig. 6.6 Distribution of bimoment, B, lateral bimoment, D, warping function, W, and lozenging function, V, along the length of a box beam with equal bimoments applied at each end. Lozenging of the profile completely inhibited at both ends

Table 6.1 Summary of functions used in the analysis of open and closed cross section beams, see equations (6.34) and (6.19)

Bending	Warping		Torsion	Lozenging
	Open cross section	*Closed cross section*		
$u = z\beta$	$u = \omega\varphi'$	$u = \chi W$	$f = \zeta_1\varphi$	$f = \zeta_2 V$
	$\omega = \int r\, ds$	$\chi = yz$	$\zeta_1 = r$	$\zeta_2 = y'z + yz'$
$J_y = \int_A z^2\, dA$	$J_\omega = \int_A \omega^2\, dA$	$a_1 = \int_A \chi^2\, dA$	$a_2 = \int_A \zeta_1^2\, dA$	$a_2 = \int_A \zeta_2^2\, dA$
				$a_3 = \int_A \zeta_1\zeta_2\, dA$
$M = EJ_y\beta'$	$B = EJ_\omega\varphi''$	$B = Ea_1 W'$	$M_D = Ga_2\varphi'$ $+ Ga_3 W$ $+ Ga_3 V'$	$D = Ga_2 V'$ $+ Ga_2 W$ $+ Ga_3\varphi'$
$M = \int_A \sigma z\, dA$	$B = \int_A \sigma\omega\, dA$	$B = \int_A \sigma\chi\, dA$	$M_D = \int_A \tau\zeta_1\, dA$	$D = \int_A \tau\zeta_2\, dA$
$\sigma = (M/J_y)z$	$\sigma = (B/J_\omega)\omega$	$\sigma = (B/a_1)\chi$	$\tau = (M_D/a_2)\zeta_1$ when $W = 0;\ V' = 0$	$\tau = (D/a_2)\zeta_2$ when $W = 0;\ \varphi' = 0$

These distributions are not very well known and it is worth noting that the equal bimoments cause opposite internal loads at the two ends so that the bimoment will be zero at the centre of the beam, as was the case for open sections in chapter 5. These effects will be useful in the frame analysis to be presented later. Some other useful relationships can also be found from the solutions which have practical applications. The relation between the bimoment and the lateral bimoment is

$$D = B' \tag{6.33}$$

Table 6.1 summarizes the displacement functions, the cross section constants, the load–displacement relations and the stresses for rectangular closed sections and compares them with similar parameters in normal bending and those already derived for open-section thin-walled beams.

For the rectangular cross sections considered, it follows from equation (6.19) that

$$\int_A \zeta_1^2\, dA = \int_A \zeta_2^2\, dA = a_2 \frac{t}{2}\, bh(b + h) \tag{6.34}$$

Equation (6.31b) shows that the bimoment depends on the cross section constant a_1 and the first derivative of the warping displacement and that it is comparable with the open section relation

$$B = EJ_\omega\varphi'' \tag{5.22}$$

where φ' is the generalized displacement associated with the generalized coordinate, ω.

There is also a parallel between the section constants given in

$$J_\omega = \int_A \omega^2 \, dA \tag{5.13}$$

and

$$a_1 = \int_A \chi^2 \, dA \tag{6.19a}$$

Effect of neglecting lozenging

The load–deformation relations are considerably simplified if the lozenging and the lateral bimoment are neglected as in references (4) and (15). Equations (6.35) give the displacements and the internal loads at any section x along the beam when the values of these parameters at $x = 0$ are known

$$\varphi(x) = \varphi_0 - \left(\frac{a_3}{a_2}\frac{l}{k}\sinh\frac{k}{l}x\right)W_0 + \left\{\frac{a_3}{a_2}\frac{1}{Ea_1}\frac{l^2}{k^2}\left(1 - \cosh\frac{k}{l}x\right)\right\}B_0$$

$$+ \frac{l^3}{Ea_1 k^3}\left(\frac{k}{l}x - \frac{a_3^2}{a_2^2}\sinh\frac{k}{l}x\right)M_{D0} \tag{a}$$

$$W(x) = \cosh\frac{k}{l}xW_0 + \left(\frac{l}{Ea_1 k}\sinh\frac{k}{l}x\right)B_0$$

$$- \left\{\frac{a_3}{a_2}\frac{1}{Ea_1}\frac{l^2}{k^2}\left(1 - \cosh\frac{k}{l}x\right)\right\}M_{D0} \tag{b}$$

$$B(x) = \left\{Ea_1\frac{k}{l}\sinh\frac{k}{l}x\right\}W_0 + \cosh\frac{k}{l}xB_0 + \frac{a_3}{a_2}\frac{l}{k}\sinh\frac{k}{l}xM_{D0} \tag{c}$$

$$M_D(x) = 1 \tag{6.35}$$

where a_1, a_2, and a_3 are given in equation (6.19), and

$$k^2 = 48\frac{G}{E}\frac{l^2}{(b+h)^2} \tag{6.36}$$

The distribution of the bimoment and the warping function along the

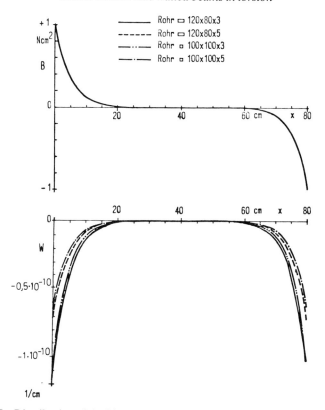

Fig. 6.7 **Distribution of the bimoment and warping function along a beam with a non-deformable profile; loads as in Fig. 6.6**

beam according to equation (6.35) are shown in Fig. 6.7. The effect of neglecting the lozenging can therefore be seen by comparing Figs 6.6 and 6.7. This approximation also applies to thick-walled box beams, which have a very small lozenging deformation in torsion.

Circular cross section tubes
The same basic theory can be used for round tubes, although there is no coupling between torsion and warping or between torsion and lozenging. This is usually referred to as the 'plane sections remain plane' condition.

It means that in equation (6.31a) a_3 becomes

$$a_{30} = 0 \qquad (6.37)$$

so that only one term remains, and

$$M_D = Ga_2\varphi' \qquad (6.38)$$

also

$$a_{20} = J_t = 2\pi r_m^3 t \qquad (6.39)$$

for thin walled circular tubes with mean radius r_m.

Out-of-plane warping will still occur due to longitudinal loads and equation (6.2) still applies. The coordinate round the circumference becomes s_0 and the warping function is now

$$\chi_0 = \tfrac{1}{2}r_m^2 \sin 2\,\frac{s_0}{r_m} \qquad (6.40)$$

This is a sinusoidal distribution with a half wave for each quarter of the circumference. From equation (6.19a) a_{10} becomes

$$a_{10} = \frac{\pi}{4}\,tr_m^5 \qquad (6.41)$$

The load–displacement relations of equation (6.35) are simplified, as in reference (4), with a_1, a_2, and a_3 replaced by a_{10}, a_{20}, and a_{30}, also, equation (6.36) becomes

$$k_0^2 = \frac{Ga_{20}}{Ea_{10}}\,l^2 \qquad (6.42)$$

There is a further simplification since, because warping and torsion are decoupled, $a_{30} = 0$ as in equation (6.37).

7

Stiffness matrix of thin walled beams

The flexibility and stiffness matrices for beams in frameworks with stiff joints were derived in chapter 4. The state variables at the ends of the beam elements, i.e., at the joints, were established using transfer matrices. The torsional stiffness of the beam elements was first defined in terms of the St Venant torsion constant, J_t, whereas, to represent more practical designs it should be the value for complete warping inhibition at the ends of the beam. For open section beams equations (5.31a) and (5.31c) with $\varphi_0' = 0$ and the condition of equal and opposite bimoments at the two ends of the beam element the effective torsion constant for complete inhibition of warping is

$$J_t^* = J_t \, \frac{al/2}{al/2 \, - \, \tanh \, al/2} \qquad (7.1)$$

as derived in reference (5). The condition of equal and opposite bi-moments at the ends of the beam implies that at the centre of the beam where $x = \frac{1}{2}, B = 0$.

From the second theorem of Bredt the torsion constant for closed section beam elements, assuming free warping, is

$$J_{tB} = \frac{E}{G} \, a_1 \, \frac{k^2}{l^2}$$

The complete warping inhibition case can be derived from equations (6.35a) and (6.35c) to give the effective torsion constant

$$J_{tB}^* = J_{tB} \, \frac{k/2}{k/2 \, - \, a_3^2/a_2^2 \, \tanh \, k/2} \qquad (7.2)$$

with k, a_1, a_2, and a_3 from equations (6.36) and (6.19), or for round tubes from equations (6.42), (6.39), and (6.41). For a closed-section cross member in a chassis frame the torsion constant for complete warping inhibition is only a few percent greater than the Bredt value. However, the difference in the case of open-section cross members is very great. As can be seen from equation (7.1) the effective torsion constant for inhibited warping is much greater than the St Venant constant.

When the exact formula for warping inhibition is included in matrix methods, both the stiffness and flexibility matrices must be increased in size from the matrices given in chapter 4. The rates of twist φ_1' and φ_2' are added to the displacements, and the bimoments B_1 and B_2 are added to the loads. Since these effects are dominant, especially in the case of open sections, the beam element matrices are enlarged by the relations derived in chapter 5.

Chassis frame designs which incorporate closed-section cross members usually have open-section side members and open sections for other cross members. Therefore the flexibility matrices of closed-section cross members have to be included in frame analysis, as in chapter 12.2.1, where, amongst others, equation (12.51) shows the matrix terms.

The flexibility matrix of equation (4.16) has to be enlarged for open section beams by including the warping terms in the matrix of equation (5.32). The displacements at the ends of the beam become

$$\mathbf{v}_h = \{u_h \ \beta_{y1h} \ \beta_{y2h} \ \beta_{z1h} \ \beta_{z2h} \ \varphi_h \ \varphi_{1h}' \ \varphi_{2h}'\} \qquad (7.3)$$

and the corresponding loads

$$\mathbf{p}_h = \{N_h \ M_{y1h} \ M_{y2h} \ M_{z1h} \ M_{z2h} \ M_{Dh} \ B_{1h} \ B_{2h}\} \qquad (7.4)$$

If the sixth row and column are omitted from the matrix $\mathbf{F}_h$ in equation (4.16a) it only contains the direct, normal and bending loads. The remaining 5×5 matrix, called $\mathbf{F}_{NM}$, is joined with the matrix of equation (5.32) to form a diagonal matrix

$$\mathbf{F}_h = \begin{bmatrix} \mathbf{F}_{NM} & \\ & \mathbf{F}_{Wt} \end{bmatrix} \qquad (7.5)$$

where $\mathbf{F}_{Wt}$ is the name given to the matrix of equation (5.32) and the new flexibility matrix for the beam element is again called $\mathbf{F}_h$ which connects the displacements in (7.3) with the loads in (7.4).

The stiffness matrix has to be arranged in terms of the node displacements as shown in chapter 4.3. The inclusion of warping terms in the displacements and loads in the beam element, h, increases equations (4.38) and (4.39) to

$$\mathbf{v}_h = \{u_{1h} \ v_{1h} \ w_{1h} \ \varphi_{1h} \ \varphi_{1h}' \ \beta_{y1h} \ \beta_{z1h}$$
$$u_{2h} \ v_{2h} \ w_{2h} \ \varphi_{2h} \ \varphi_{2h}' \ \beta_{y2h} \ \beta_{z2h}\} \qquad (7.6)$$

and

$$\mathbf{p}_h = \{ N_{1h} \ Q_{y1h} \ Q_{z1h} \ M_{D1h} \ B_{1h} \ M_{y1h} \ M_{z1h}$$
$$N_{2h} \ Q_{y2h} \ Q_{z2h} \ M_{D2h} \ B_{2h} \ M_{y2h} \ M_{z2h} \} \qquad (7.7)$$

The rate of twist φ' relates to the relative displacement of undeformed cross sections. This implies that parallel lines in, say, the flanges of a channel section remain parallel but are displaced longitudinally giving rise to warping. Warping is not linked to any of the coordinate directions which have to be considered for compatibility across the joints, as can be seen from the transformation matrices in chapter 8. However, it is useful to place φ', the rate of twist, in the column of displacements immediately following the angle of twist, φ, in the stiffness matrix.

The load–displacement equation for warping can be expressed as

$$\{ M_{D1} \ B_1 \ M_{D2} \ B_2 \} = \mathbf{K}_{Wt} \{ \varphi_1 \ \varphi_1' \ \varphi_2 \ \varphi_2' \} \qquad (7.8)$$

where $\mathbf{K}_{Wt}$ is the stiffness sub-matrix of the warping terms and can be obtained from equation (5.31) as

$$\mathbf{K}_{Wt} = \frac{\eta}{al \sin al - 2(\cosh al - 1)} \times$$

$$
\begin{bmatrix}
\alpha \sinh al & \cosh al - 1 & -\alpha \sinh al & \cos al - 1 \\[2mm]
\cosh al - 1 & l \cosh al - \dfrac{1}{\alpha} \sinh al & -(\cosh al - 1) & \dfrac{1}{\alpha} \sinh al - l \\[2mm]
-\alpha \sinh al & -(\cosh al - 1) & \alpha \sinh al & -(\cosh al - 1) \\[2mm]
\cosh al - 1 & \dfrac{1}{\alpha} \sinh al - l & -(\cosh al - 1) & l \cosh al - \dfrac{1}{\alpha} \sinh al
\end{bmatrix}
$$

$$(7.9)$$

This matrix can be split again into sub-matrices as in chapter 4

$$
\mathbf{K}_{Wt} = \left[
\begin{array}{c|c}
\mathbf{K}_{WtI} & \mathbf{K}_{WtII}^{T} \\
\hline
\mathbf{K}_{WtII} & \mathbf{K}_{WtIII}
\end{array}
\right] \qquad (7.10)
$$

In order to bring together the beam stiffness matrix equation (4.41) and the matrix of warping terms, the matrix in equation (4.41) is split into sub-matrices $K_{ik \atop ln}$ for the section from row i to row k and column l to column n of the matrix K_h, for example

$$\mathbf{K}_{56 \atop 23} = \frac{E}{l_h} \begin{bmatrix} 0 & -6\,\dfrac{J_y}{l_h} \\ 6\,\dfrac{J_z}{l_h} & 0 \end{bmatrix} \qquad (7.11)$$

This abbreviated notation allows the repetitive and symmetrical nature of the stiffness matrix to be seen at a glance, e.g., $\mathbf{K}_{79 \atop 13} = -\mathbf{K}_{13 \atop 13}$. Also it means that $\mathbf{K}_{13 \atop 13}$ can be inserted repeatedly. The whole stiffness matrix $\mathbf{K}_h$ can now be written for the beam element, including warping terms, as

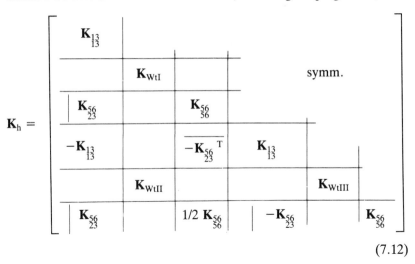

$$\qquad (7.12)$$

This stiffness matrix connects the column matrix of displacements at the ends of the beam element in equation (7.6) with the loads in the column matrix (7.7). For the beam element h, the parameters η_h, α_h, l_h, have to be used in place of those used in equation (7.9).

8

Joints

So far, in this treatment of chassis frames and three dimensional frameworks, it has been assumed that the beam elements meet at point nodes or joints. In this type of structure the elastic properties of the joints are as important as those of the beams. Normally it is assumed that the beams meet at discrete points for all types of joint and that the beams have constant cross-sectional properties. It is shown in this chapter that there are different beam axes for the various generalized forces and displacements, and these have to be taken into account in order to avoid serious errors.

It is well known that direct loads which do not act along the axis of the centroid of the cross section cause bending moments in a beam. Similarly, normal loads which do not act through the shear or torsion centre cause torques and, as shown in chapter 5, direct loads which do not act through the points of zero warping cause bimoments. An exception to this is when two equal direct loads act in the same direction at points with equal and opposite values of unit warping displacement. In this case the effects cancel each other out, e.g., F_1 and F_2 in Fig. 8.1. Neither a bending moment nor a bimoment is produced when two equal direct loads, F_3 and F_4, act in the same direction in the vertical plane through the neutral axis of the section. When there are equal and opposite direct loads not acting through the zero warping points they produce both a bending moment and a bimoment, as shown by the couple F_5 and F_6. Finally, it is shown in chapter 5 that couples made up of normal or lateral loads whose plane does not pass through the torsion centre produce bimoments, as in Fig. 5.7. Therefore it is not correct to use the intersections of the centroid axes as nodes without noting the effect of the intersections of the torsion centre axes and the zero warping lines along the beams. The zero warping lines are lines parallel to the axis of the beam passing through the points of zero warping in the cross section, particularly in the flanges of channel sections.

When assembling the total stiffness matrix used in the matrix displacement method, described in chapter 4.3, the effect of the different axes must be included. This is done by transforming the non-coincident load

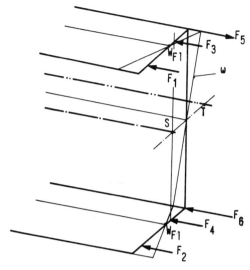

Fig. 8.1   **Internal loads caused by external direct loads on the end of a channel section.**
$F_1 + F_2$ **causes a zero bimoment but a lateral bending moment.**
$F_3 + F_4$ **causes a zero bimoment and a zero bending moment.**
The couple F_5 and F_6 causes both bimoment and vertical bending moment

and displacement components into the axes defined for the node. In the case of the matrix force method, however, the lack of coincidence of the axes is taken into account when the end loads are analysed, i.e., in the derivation of the B_0 and B_1 matrices given in chapters 4, section 4.2, and 12.

8.1   THE COMPATIBILITY CONDITIONS AT JOINTS

If the beams in a structure are represented by their centroid axes, the ends of the beam elements at joints are defined as being at the intersection of these axes. If the centroid axes do not intersect, a plane can be formed by moving one axis parallel to itself until it intersects the other axis. The intersection of the projections of the centroid axes normal to this plane will define the ends of the beams. Generally the intersections of the torsion axes and the zero warping axes will not be at the ends of the beam elements defined in this way. The zero warping axis is defined as the axis formed by the intersection of the plane containing the zero warping lines in the flanges and the plane containing the centroid and torsion axes. A node must therefore be defined by more than one point and the torsion centre, T, the centroid, S, and the warping point, W, at the end of one of the beam elements meeting at the joint are used for this definition. Such a node is called a *TSW* node. The warping point W is the point where the zero warping axis meets the end plane of the beam. For example, in Fig. 8.2 the *TSW* node is defined by these points in the end plane of the channel-section beam with a vertical web, called the vertical channel. The corresponding three points in the end plane of the channel-section beam with a horizontal web, called the horizontal channel, are T_Q, S_Q, and W_Q. The centroids of the two channels S and S_Q are separated vertically by the distance h_s.

The loads and displacements at the beam ends are defined in terms of the end of the vertical channel, i.e., the *TSW* node. For the horizontal

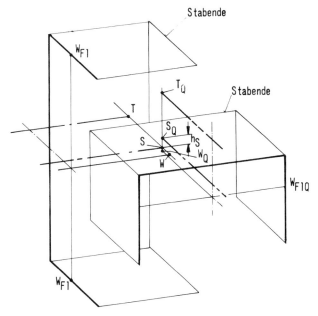

Fig. 8.2 An example of a joint defined by a *TSW* node at the end of the vertical channel.
['Stabende' = 'end plane of beam'.]

channel these parameters are required at the $T_Q S_Q W_Q$ node. It is only possible to assemble the total stiffness matrix when the stiffness matrix $\mathbf{K}_{QQ}$ relating to $T_Q S_Q W_Q$ is transformed to the matrix $\mathbf{K}_Q$ relating to the *TSW* node which is defined in global coordinates. If the displacements of the nodal points in global coordinates, i.e., those at the end of the beam defining the joint, are denoted by the column matrix, $\mathbf{d}$, while the displacements of the nodal points at the end of the secondary beam, here the horizontal channel, are denoted by $\mathbf{v}_Q$, the transformation matrix, $\mathbf{T}_d$, is defined by

$$\mathbf{v}_Q = \mathbf{T}_d \mathbf{d} \tag{8.1}$$

If the loads on the secondary beam corresponding to $\mathbf{d}$ are denoted by $\mathbf{f}_Q$ and the loads corresponding to $\mathbf{v}_Q$ are denoted by $\mathbf{p}_Q$, the transformation matrix $\mathbf{T}_f$ will be given by

$$\mathbf{f}_Q = \mathbf{T}_f \mathbf{p}_Q \tag{8.2}$$

From equation (4.40) the relation between load and displacement vectors for the connecting beam, in this case the horizontal channel section; will be given by

$$\mathbf{p}_Q = \mathbf{K}_{QQ} \mathbf{v}_Q \tag{8.3}$$

Substituting equation (8.1) into (8.3) and pre-multiplying by $\mathbf{T}_f$, the relation

$$\mathbf{T}_f \mathbf{p}_Q = \mathbf{T}_f \mathbf{K}_{QQ} \mathbf{T}_d \mathbf{d}$$

is obtained. Substituting for the left hand side from equation (8.2) this expression becomes

$$\mathbf{f}_Q = \mathbf{K}_Q \mathbf{d} \tag{8.4}$$

where

$$\mathbf{K}_Q = \mathbf{T}_f \mathbf{K}_{QQ} \mathbf{T}_d \tag{8.5}$$

which gives the stiffness matrix of the connecting beam in terms of the main beam, i.e., in the global coordinates.

It will be shown later that

$$\mathbf{T}_f = \mathbf{T}_d^T \tag{8.6}$$

so that the transformation relationship between the stiffness matrices can be written in the normal way, as in equation (4.53), in the form

$$\mathbf{K}_Q = \mathbf{T}_d^T \mathbf{K}_{QQ} \mathbf{T}_d \tag{8.7}$$

The transformation matrix
As can be seen from Fig. 8.2, the transformation matrix, T_d, will depend on both the profile of the cross sections and the orientation of the beams meeting at the joint. In order to keep the transformation matrix small enough for practical use the derivation will be confined to beam elements meeting at right angles, as is the case for commercial vehicle chassis frames. For these frames the side members will be taken as channel sections with the webs vertical and the flanges towards the centre of the vehicle. In the case of trailers, the side members are normally 'I' section members which have T, S, and W all on the web centreline. The cross members are channel sections and may have horizontal webs with the flanges either pointing up or down, or vertical webs with the flanges pointing either to the left or right. Each of these cases must be dealt with separately.

First the transformation matrix for the system shown in Fig. 8.2 will be given, next the case with a vertical channel-section cross member is discussed, finally the general formula will be given. Figure 8.3 shows the displacements at the ends of the beams in these cases. The displacements of the nodal points at the end of the longitudinal beam element are shown in Fig. 8.3(a). Figure 8.3(b) shows the displacements at the nodal points of the horizontal channel-section cross member with the flanges pointing down. Both these diagrams refer to the case in Fig. 8.2. The third diagram, Fig. 8.3(c), shows the displacements of the nodal points of a cross member with a vertical web and the flanges pointing to the left. Figure 8.4 shows the corresponding components of the loads. For the horizontal channel cross member shown in Fig. 8.2 the transformation matrix, T_d, defined in equation (8.1) is given in full in equation (8.8) for clarity.

When the corresponding axes at the two beam ends do not intersect, the rotation about one of the axes will make a contribution to the translation of the nodal point. For instance, from Fig. 8.3(b), the displacement v_Q is at a distance $d_{TQ} + h_s$ from the centroid axis through S. The rotation β_y about the y axis of the side member, Figure 8.3(a), therefore gives a displacement $-(d_{TQ} + h_s)\beta_y$ in the v_Q direction, as in equation (8.8). The rotations about the axes at the nodal points cannot be accurately transferred across the joint because the end of the cross-member does not coincide with the plane of the zero warping points on the flanges of the side member. For example, the angle of twist of the end of the cross member φ_Q corresponds with the slope of the side member in bending β_y which takes place in the plane passing through W and not through S, see Fig. 8.3(a). The two parallel planes are separated by the distance d_w so that $d_w\varphi'_Q = -d_w\varphi'$ should be added to φ_Q, as in equation (8.8). From equation (8.8) it can be seen that $\varphi'_Q = -\varphi'$ so that for this type of cross member these rotations are compatible. Normally the bending slopes cannot be described in the plane of the zero warping points and have to be corrected by considering the warping of the end plane of the beam.

$\{$	u	v	w	φ	φ'	β_y	β_z $\}_\mathbf{d}$
u_Q		1		$-h_S$			
v_Q	-1				$-(d_{TQ}+h_S)\,d_W$	$-(d_{TQ}+h_S)$	
w_Q			1	$-d_T$			
φ_Q					$-d_W$	1	
φ'_Q					-1		
β_{yQ}			-1				
β_{zQ}					$-(h_S - d_{wQ})$		1

$\mathbf{v_Q}$ $\qquad$ $\mathbf{T_d}$

$$(8.8)$$

The load transformation matrix, $\mathbf{T_f}$, is given in full in equation (8.9) using the full expressions in equation (8.2) for the case of the horizontal channel section cross member.

$\{$	N_Q	Q_{yQ}	Q_{zQ}	M_{DQ}	B_Q	M_{yQ}	M_{zQ} $\}_{\mathbf{p_Q}}$
N		-1					
Q_y	1						
Q_z			1				
M_D	$-h_S$		$-d_T$			-1	
B		$-(d_{TQ}+h_S)\cdot d_W$		$-d_W$	-1		$-(h_S - d_{wQ})$
M_y		$-(d_{TQ}+h_S)$		1			
M_z							1

$\mathbf{f_Q}$ $\qquad$ $\mathbf{T_f}$

$$(8.9)$$

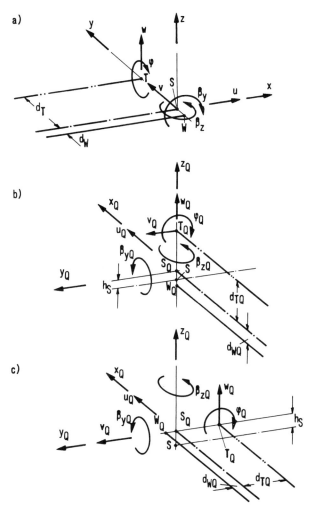

Fig. 8.3   Displacements of nodal points at the ends of beams meeting at a joint,
used to build up the matrix T_d in equation (8.8).
   (a) and (b)   Joint shown in Fig. 8.2 with a horizontal channel section
      cross member with the flanges pointing down
   (c)   Joint with a vertical channel section cross member with the flanges
      pointing to the left

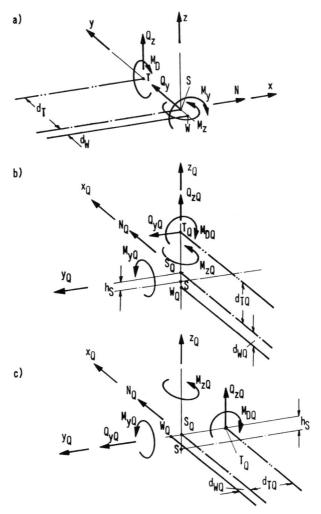

Fig. 8.4   Loads corresponding to the displacements in Fig. 8.3

The loads again have to be carried across the different axis systems with corrections for the cases where there is an offset. This is clear when a direct load has an offset since it will produce a moment. For example, the force Q_{yQ} in Fig. 8.4(b) gives a moment of $-(d_{TQ} + h_s)Q_{yQ}$ to be added to the moment M_y in Fig. 8.4(a). When direct loads or couples formed by direct loads do not act through the zero warping points they give rise to bimoments, as explained before. An example of this is the term $-(d_{TQ} + h_s)d_W Q_{yQ}$ in the expression for B in equation (8.9) which is obtained directly from equation (5.20).

The general matrix transformation equation (8.6) can be confirmed by comparing the terms of $\mathbf{T_d}$ in equation (8.8) and $\mathbf{T_f}$ in equation (8.9), where it can be seen that one is the transform of the other. Similarly, for the case of a vertical channel cross member with the flanges pointing to the left, see Fig. 8.3(c), equation (8.10) replaces equation (8.8), and the matrix $\mathbf{T_f}$ is again the transform of the corresponding matrix, $\mathbf{T_d}$.

$\{$	u	v	w	φ	φ'	β_y	β_z $\}_d$
u_Q		1		$-h_s$			
v_Q	-1				$-h_s\,d_w$	$-h_s$	
w_Q			1	$-d_T$		$-d_{TQ}$	
φ_Q $=$					d_w	1	
φ'_Q					1		
β_{yQ}				-1	$-d_{wQ}$		
β_{zQ}					$-h_s$		1

$$\mathbf{v_Q} \qquad\qquad \mathbf{T_d}$$

$$(8.10)$$

The discussion of the transformation matrices for the ends of the cross members shows that they depend on both the orientation of the web and the direction in which the flanges point. These conditions also apply to the channel section side members where they have the flanges of the two sides pointing inwards. Therefore the $\mathbf{T_d}$ matrices are different for the left and right hand sides of a ladder frame. Figure 8.5 shows the distances from the centroid axes and their sign convention for the joints of the left hand side member (top), a channel section cross member with horizontal web and downward pointing flanges (centre left), a channel section cross member with vertical web and leftward pointing flanges (centre right) and a right hand side member (bottom). The transformation matrix given in equation (8.11) can then be applied to all situations if the sign of the terms in rows

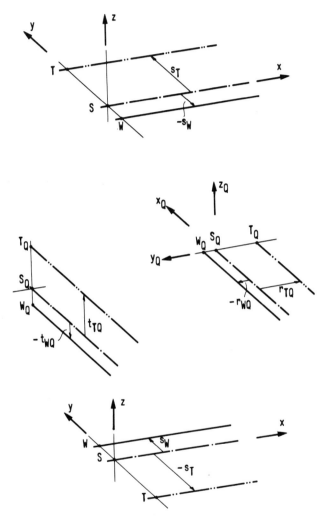

Fig. 8.5   Distances of the torsion axes and the warping point axes from the centroid axis for various joint configurations, used to build up the matrix in equation (8.11). See text for definitions

4 and 5 of column 5, (the 45 and 55 elements of the matrix), is taken to be the upper sign for cross members with vertical webs and the lower sign for those with horizontal webs.

$$
\mathbf{T_d} = \begin{bmatrix}
 & 1 & & -h_S & & & \\
-1 & & & & (h_S + t_{TQ})s_W & -(h_S + t_{TQ}) & \\
 & & 1 & -s_T & & -r_{TQ} & \\
 & & & & \mp s_W & 1 & \\
 & & & & \pm 1 & & \\
 & & & -1 & r_{WQ} & & \\
 & & & & -(h_S + t_{WQ}) & & 1
\end{bmatrix}
$$

$$(8.11)$$

In all cases the dimension h_s is positive when S_Q is above S.

8.2 THE FLEXIBILITY OF JOINTS

In structural analysis the nodes are usually taken as rigid, the 'stiff joint' assumption in framework analysis. In fact the joints deform under load as well as the beams. It is clear that this effect will be more important for short beams, where the length of the beam elements is the same order as the cross section dimension of the beam or the dimension across the nodal area. The cross members and the sections of the side members between the cross members of chassis frames can be regarded as short beams in this context.

Rate of twist flexibility
In the case of torsionally flexible frames, the rate of twist flexibility of the joints has considerable influence on the torsional stiffness of the whole frame. The rate of twist flexibility of a joint can be included in the analysis of chassis frames by the matrix force method by a rate of twist flexibility coefficient, as shown in chapter 12.2.2. This coefficient can be defined as the change in rate of twist between the boundaries of a node between a side member and a cross member when transmitting a unit bimoment (1 Ncm^2). Since a frame can carry a load when the beam elements only

84 *The analysis of commercial vehicle structures*

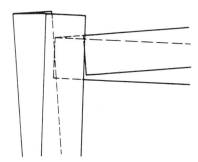

Fig. 8.6 Gaps occurring if two channel sections meet at right angles with uninhibited warping

carry direct loads, lateral loads, bending moments, and torques, the bimoments at the joints will be statically indeterminate. When two beam elements meet at a joint there will be one unknown bimoment. The values of the unknowns can be found as usual from the compatibility condition of closing a cut in the structure.

This can best be demonstrated by the example of two channel-section beams connected at the flanges. If the rate of twist of the beams is not coupled, as would be the case for uninhibited warping, the gap shown in Fig. 8.6 results. In order to allow uninhibited warping the joint would have to be designed as in Fig. 8.7(a). To obtain a statically determinate frame, joints must release the statically indeterminate displacements, e.g., the slope due to a redundant bending moment. In Fig. 8.7(a) the zero warping lines of the cross member Q are extended as far as the imaginary bimoment joint axis BGA. This axis is defined such that longitudinal forces in the flanges of the side member L do not give rise to bimoments. Therefore, the ends of the zero warping lines of Q lie in the plane of the zero warping lines of L. In this case torque is transferred across the joint without the introduction of bimoments. Such a joint can be called an 'ideal bimoment joint' as opposed to joints which uncouple the rates of twist in the beams and cause problems for the remaining generalized displacements. If the axis BGA is assumed to be at the outer edge of the flanges of beam L, for example, a rate of twist in beam L would cause a rotation in beam Q. This arrangement might appear to be an advantage since the imagined extension of Q (as far as the zero warping lines of beam L) would not be necessary.

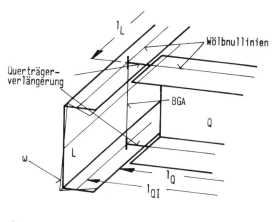

a)

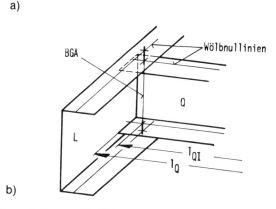

b)

Fig. 8.7   Layouts for two ideal bimoment joints.
['Wölbnullinen' = 'zero warping line'; 'Querträger-verlängerung' =
'extension of the cross member zero warping lines'.]

To distinguish between the actual beam lengths l_L and l_Q which will lead
to a joint boundary where warping inhibition occurs and the lengths
associated with an ideal bimoment joint, the length of the cross member
between the *BGA* axes is called l_{QI}. The length of the side member
element remains the same, as can be seen in Fig. 8.7(a), since the *BGA*
axis is in the cross section of the side member which includes the zero
warping lines of the cross member. This method of analysis is better than
the method using the transformation matrices given in equations (8.8)–

(8.11) for very short beams, such as chassis cross members, where it is important that the actual length of the beam be used.

To take a further example, Fig. 8.7(b) shows a joint where the cross member is attached to the web of the side member, in this case $l_Q > l_{QI}$. A torque is initiated in Q due to bending in L at distance $l_{QI} - l_Q$ from the end of the beam. This causes a bimoment which is the product of this distance and the torque on the cross member. This bimoment is called the transfer bimoment and is used in chapter 12.2.1.

The flexibility of joints has an important bearing on the compatibility of structures under load. The analysis is based on the idea of closing imaginary cuts as illustrated in Fig. 8.8 where the ends of the beams in the joint of Fig. 8.6 are shown in the cut position with the bimoments required to bring them together. Flexibility in the joint causes a reduction in the bimoments required to close the cuts, which, in turn, causes a reduction in strains warping the beams.

The rate of twist flexibility of a joint can be represented by the quantity

$$\delta_{LQF}$$

which is the difference between the rates of twist at the ends of the beams L and Q when transferring a unit bimoment of 1 Ncm^2. The flexibility of various joints can easily be compared using this simple quantity, and it is also used to introduce joint flexibility in the matrix force method of analysing frames, as shown in chapter 12.2.2. Figure 8.9 compares the rate of twist flexibility of a number of joints where the channel section used for the side member has the dimensions 80/200/80 × 6 mm. The dimensions of the various cross members are given in the figure. This figure is taken from reference (11). It is also shown in that reference that

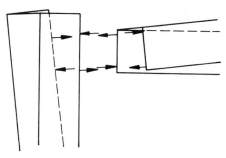

Fig. 8.8   Bimoments required to close the gap shown in Fig. 8.7

Table 8.1   Additional details of the cross sections used to make up the joints in Fig. 8.9

Joint No.	Cross Member	Wall Thickness	Thickness of gusset plate (mm)	Width	b = Bolted W = Welded
1 2 3	33 — 68,5 — 92 mm	4	·Alligator 6	130 70	b
4 5	⌐80 / ⌐200	6	Welded to flange 6	70	b
6	⌐120 / 188	6	–	–	b
7, 8	60 / 140	6	–	–	w
9	120 / 176	6	6	160	b
10	150 / 176	6	6	180	b
11	60/140 50/80	6 6	6 –	131 114 –	w w
12	65 / 160 60 / 140	7 6	8, 6, 4 6	170 ÷ 52 47	w w
13	60 / 140	6	–	–	w
14	60 / 140	6	6	171 91	b
15, 16	60 / 140	6	6	131 51	b
17	60 / 120	6	–	–	w
18	50/100 50/100	5	5	140	b
19	50 / 100	5	5	130 ÷ 40	w
20	60 / 80	6	–	–	w

88   *The analysis of commercial vehicle structures*

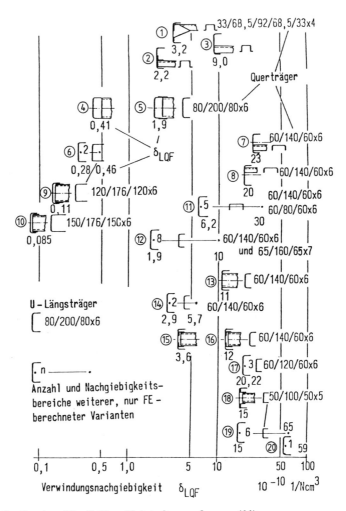

Fig. 8.9   **Torsional flexibility of joints from reference (11).**
['Querträger' = 'cross member'; 'Langsträger' = 'side member';
'Anzahl und . . .', = 'Additional joints calculated by finite element
methods'; 'Verwindungsnachgiebigkeit = 'rate of twist flexibility'.]

joints with values of δ_{LQF} stiffer than 10^{-11} and more flexible than 10^{-8} have little influence on the torsional stiffness of a commercial vehicle chassis frame. The flexibilities in Fig. 8.9 were obtained from finite element calculations and verified by experiment on at least one sample of each type of joint.

Flexibility in bending and torsion

The effect of joint flexibility in the transfer of bending and torsion at a joint can also be represented by a single parameter. This parameter gives the difference between the twist of the side member and the slope at the end of the cross member or the slope of the side member and the twist at the end of the cross member meeting at the joint when transferring a unit moment. These flexibilities cannot be directly inserted into compatibility relationships and, therefore, they are inserted into the relations for the bending of beam elements. The use of nodal substructures in chapter 9 and chapter 12, sections 12.2 and 12.3, includes the effect of these flexibilities. Reference (**16**) gives a definition of a stiffness constant for a joint with bending flexibility and shows how it is included in the beam-element stiffness matrix.

The joint element

The rate of twist stiffness of a joint cannot be introduced into the matrix displacement method of analysis in such a simple way as the rate of twist flexibility is introduced into the matrix force method. In this case it is necessary to complete the definition of the *TSW* node, considered in section 8.1 above, by including a node boundary at the end of beam Q. Since the beams are represented by their centroid axes, the end of beam Q lies at the centroid of beam L (point S_L in Fig. 8.10). To take into account the effect of the whole joint in this system where the joints are normally discrete points it is necessary to introduce joint elements. The stiffness matrix for such a joint element can be obtained from a finite element analysis of the joint area. The extent of this area is determined empirically and, for the side member, it extends beyond the edge of the cross member by 0.7 and 0.8 times the height of the side member, as shown in Fig. 8.10. To find the internal loads in the joint element the displacements at one boundary are fixed and unit displacements made successively at the nodes of the other boundary. The unit displacements are

$$u \quad v \quad w \quad \varphi \quad \varphi' \quad \beta_y \quad \beta_z$$

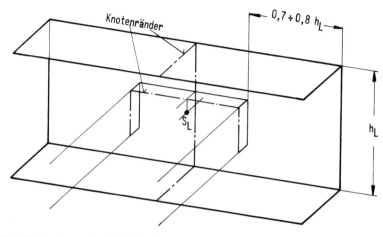

Fig. 8.10   Example of a joint element.
['Knotenränder' = 'ends of the beam elements'.]

while the internal loads at both boundaries are found by a finite element analysis to be

$$N \ Q_y \ Q_z \ M_D \ B \ M_y \ M_z$$

A joint or nodal stiffness matrix obtained in this way gives an understanding of the bending and torsion properties of the joint. Naturally the transformation relationships defined in section 8.1 do not apply when a joint element is used.

9

Finite element analysis of joints

To obtain a satisfactory analysis when the joints of a chassis frame are idealized as point nodes, the compatibility of the deformation of the ends of the beams meeting at the joint has to be maintained, even when the joints are assumed to be flexible. The fact that this is still an approximate idealization becomes clear when the dimensions of the joints are compared with the dimensions of the beam elements connecting them. Satisfactory results can only be expected when the nodal areas are not too large compared with the cross sectional dimensions of the beam elements. The approximation made by assuming point nodes is only accurate for finding the overall deformation of the chassis frame and the internal loads in the cross sections of the beams. This implies that the internal loads will only be accurate up to the boundary of a joint area, for instance up to the edge of a plate or gusset used to reinforce the joint, or up to the cross section where rivetting or welding is carried out. Near the boundary of the joint the stresses will deviate from those calculated for the beam element. It is obvious that it is not possible to analyse the stress distribution within the area of the joint using the assumption of point nodes. To find these stresses it is necessary to use a separate finite element analysis. In this case the ends of the beam elements are assumed to be at the boundary of the joint, as opposed to the assumption in chapter 8.2 where they were taken as being within the actual joint area. Figure 9.1 shows an example of a finite joint area drawn as a sub-structure with the plate elements required for a finite element analysis drawn in and with the internal loads shown at one of the three boundaries of the joint. The finite element analysis of the joint will give the internal loads and displacements at the nodes of the plate elements, and these have to be idealized into the state variables at the ends of the beam elements used for the analysis of the whole frame by the matrix force method.

The displacements at the boundary of the sub-structure are, from Fig. 9.2, $u, v, w, \varphi, \varphi', \beta_y$, and β_z, for joints 1 and 3, with β_x instead of β_y in the case of joint 2.

The displacement vector corresponding to equation (4.14) can be

91

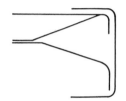

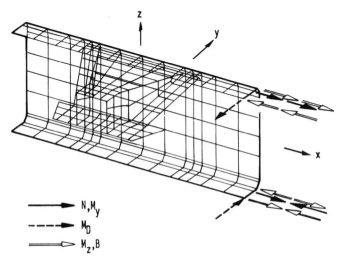

Fig. 9.1   Finite element mesh for a joint with an alligator cross member

written, if s is the number of the sub-structure, as

$$\mathbf{v}_s = \{u_{1s}\ u_{2s}\ u_{3s}\ \beta_{y1s}\ \beta_{x2s}\ \beta_{y3s}\ \beta_{z1s}\ \beta_{z2s}\ \beta_{z3s}\ \varphi_{1s}\ \varphi_{2s}\ \varphi_{3s}\ \varphi'_{1s}\ \varphi'_{2s}\ \varphi'_{3s}\} \tag{9.1}$$

The internal load vector corresponding to equation (4.15) is, from Fig. 9.2

$$\mathbf{p}_s = \{N_{1s}\ N_{2s}\ N_{3s}\ M_{y1s}\ M_{x2s}\ M_{y3s}\ M_{z1s}\ M_{z2s}\ M_{z3s}\ M_{D1s}\ M_{D2s}\ M_{D3s}\ \\ B_{1s}\ B_{2s}\ B_{3s}\} \tag{9.2}$$

with the flexibility matrix $\mathbf{F}_s$ defined by

$$\mathbf{v}_s = \mathbf{F}_s \mathbf{p}_s \tag{9.3}$$

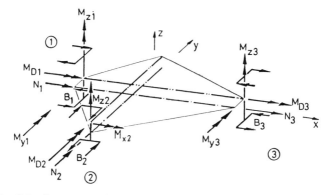

Fig. 9.2   Internal load systems at the edges of a joint substructure

The joints of the rear cross member have only two boundaries with a corresponding reduction in displacements and internal loads, as shown in chapter 12, section 12.2.

The complete frame analysis with joint sub-structures is given in chapter 12, sections 12.2 and 12.3. The deformation of the whole frame as well as the internal loads in the beam elements and the stresses in the joint sub-structures found from the finite element analysis are given. It is important to note that finite element analysis should only be used for those areas where normal analytical methods cannot be used. In particular, beam elements where the cross section remains constant should not be analysed using a finite element method.

Deformation
The fairly simple joint of Fig. 9.3 is used to show the way the internal loads and the supports are introduced into the finite element model of a joint. As far as flexibility is concerned this joint could be treated as a point node joint. The mesh chosen is the minimum possible to give reasonable results. The mesh lines in the flange include the zero warping lines and the lines where the vertical plane through centroid axis cuts the flange. The direct load, N, acting on the cross section can be introduced as two equal loads at the ends of these latter lines. The horizontal bending moments are introduced as pairs of unit loads at the edges of the flange, as shown by the loads labelled M_z in Fig. 9.3(a). The bimoments, B, are introduced as four unit loads at the edges of the flanges, see Fig. 9.3(b). The bending

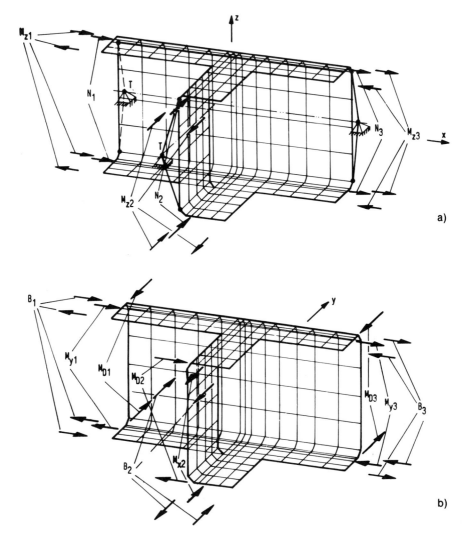

**Fig. 9.3   Internal loads introduced at the substructure boundaries and supports
and the minimum mesh that can be used for a finite element analysis of a
simple joint between two channel sections.**
(a)   Horizontal bending
(b)   Torsion

moments M_x and M_y acting about the x and y axes are introduced as unit loads acting through the zero warping lines, as shown in Fig. 9.3(b). The torques, M_D, are shown as equal and opposite unit loads acting in the plane of the flanges, again shown in Fig. 9.3(b). Experimental evidence has shown that there is no advantage in using more finite element nodes to transfer the internal loads in the beam elements to the joint. The matrix displacement method gives smaller displacements than the actual ones when compatible elements are used. It is possible to compensate for this effect by introducing concentrated loads at the points chosen. Therefore the method given above for transferring the beam loads to the joint is to be preferred to any alternative method.

The substructure must be supported for the finite element analysis and rigid supports are chosen at the torsion centres of the members comprising the joint at the boundaries of the joint area. These are joined to the beams by the pin-jointed rigid bars shown in Fig. 9.3(a). Two of these supports are shown as T in Fig. 9.3(a), with the third not labelled. The vector of loads, $\mathbf{p}_s$ given in equation (9.2) does not contain these support loads because they are shear forces which are eliminated by equilibrium conditions. In order to find the flexibility matrix, $\mathbf{F}_s$, all the boundary displacements are calculated for a unit value of each internal load at the boundaries of the joint.

In the case of the joint shown in Fig. 9.3 the centroid and torsion axes of both the cross member and side member lie in the same plane. This is a special case, but it often occurs in the design of the rear cross member of a chassis frame. In this special case the loads induced by lateral bending and torsion are uncoupled, so that the flexibility matrices can be calculated for each of the load cases separately and combined to make up the flexibility matrix of the whole nodal area. When cross members with horizontal webs are used, the centroid and torsion axes are not in the same plane, as shown in Fig. 8.2, and the flexibility matrix is completely filled. Figure 9.4 shows the supports used for the finite element model in this case.

The displacements defined in the cross section in equation (9.1) can be found by using the displacements at the positions where the internal loads in the beam elements are assumed to be transferred to the nodal area.

The compatibility condition at the boundaries between the beam elements and the nodal area is only approximately fulfilled by the idealization proposed here. The behaviour of the nodal substructures is determined in each case by the transfer of loads at the boundaries and the

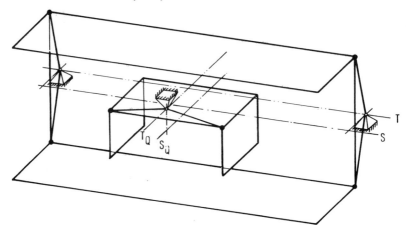

Fig. 9.4   Support system for a joint substructure with a channel section cross member with a horizontal web

values of the displacements in the cross sections of the beams at the boundaries of the joint nodal area. This means that, compared with the usual substructure analysis where the load–displacement relations at the boundaries are known for the finite element nodes, these relationships depend on the elastic properties of the two parts of the structure. For an accurate substructure analysis, the ends of the beam elements and the boundaries of the nodal substructures should be straight lines after deformation, as they represent the warped ends of the cross sections, and the shape of these cross sections should be undeformed. Such constraints could be imposed on the finite element analysis, as shown in reference **(6)**, where a method of retaining linear boundaries is given.

Imposed constraints always reduce the flexibility of a structure. While this principle must be mentioned, it has been proved that, for the analysis of chassis frames, the effect is not important when calculating the overall load–deflection characteristics. Therefore, the condition that the ends of the beam elements shall be made up of straight lines need not be enforced when assembling the flexibility matrix, $\mathbf{F}_s$; see reference **(11)**. To prevent the deformation of the cross sections of the beams at the substructure boundaries, additional pin-jointed members can be inserted in the planes of the boundaries.

The requirement that the compatibility conditions at the boundaries of the nodal substructures should be approximately correct means that the nodal area of the substructure must be sufficiently large as the loads must be spread according to St Venant's principle. Based on experience, this means that the length of the beams included in the joint area should be 0.8 times the height of the side-member section.

It is difficult to compare the flexibilities of different nodes using this method, because the terms in the F_s are not readily accessible, whereas the point node assumption leads to explicit flexibility coefficients. However, Table 9.1 does give flexibilities which correspond approximately

Table 9.1 Elements of the substructure flexibility matrix which correspond approximately to the coefficients obtained from the point node assumption

$$\{ \cdots \quad M_{x2} \quad \cdots \quad M_{z2} \quad \cdots \quad M_{D2} \quad \cdots \quad B_2 \quad \cdot \}_{P_s}$$

	M_{x2}		M_{z2}		M_{D2}		B_2	
$\cdots$					$\beta_{y1\,MD2}$			
$\beta_{x2\,Mx2}$								
					$\beta_{y3\,MD2}$			
			$\beta_{z1\,Mz2}$					
			$\beta_{z2\,Mz2}$					
			$\beta_{z3\,Mz2}$					
$\varphi_{1\,Mx2}$								
$\varphi_{3\,Mx2}$					$\varphi_{2\,MD2}$			
							$\varphi'_{1\,B2}$	
							$\varphi'_{2\,B2}$	
							$\varphi'_{3\,B2}$	

$$F_s$$

with the flexibility coefficients of the other method. For example, φ'_{1B2} is the rate of twist at the boundary of sub-structure 1 caused by a unit bimoment at boundary 2, and has the dimension

$$\frac{1}{N \, cm^3} \; \overline{}$$

and the flexibility is approximately

$$\delta_{LQF} \approx \varphi'_{2B2} - \frac{\varphi'_{1B2} + \varphi'_{3B2}}{2} \tag{9.4}$$

The right hand side of equation (9.4) involves the twisting of the substructure from the nodal point to the boundaries of the nodal area, whereas δ_{LQF} only gives the changes in the rate of twist between the cross member and the side member. In order to find the nodal flexibility coefficients exactly from the flexibility matrix it is necessary to include the deformations of the side member and the cross member from the boundaries of the nodal area to the original node point, since in the complete frame analysis using point nodes, beam elements are used which extend up to the points defined as the nodes.

Stresses
The simple joint between a cross member and a side member shown in Fig. 9.3 has been analysed using a finer finite element mesh, as shown in Fig. 9.5 where the section of frame with a central cross member is subjected to the longitudinal load F at the centre of the cross member. This load puts the joint in horizontal bending. The coarse meshing of Fig. 9.3 is only sufficient for analysing the flexibilities of the whole structure, whereas the fine mesh of Fig. 9.5 is needed to find the detailed stress distribution in the joint necessary for a comparison with experiment. Figure 9.6 shows the comparison between measured and theoretical stress distributions across the flanges of beams at the sections shown. The theoretical values of the direct stresses in both the lateral and longitudinal directions and the shear stresses were found by using a matrix displacement method. Figure 9.6(a) shows the magnitude and direction of the principal stresses, while Fig. 9.6(b) shows the stress distribution using the Huber–von Mises representation. The small differences between the direct stresses on the inner and outer surfaces are due, in this case, to local bending of the flanges. Another frequent cause of these

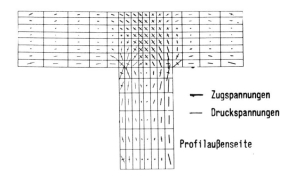

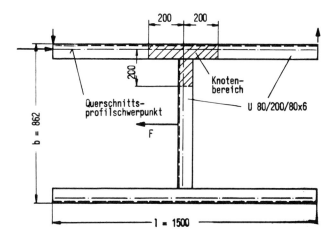

Fig. 9.5   Principal stresses in the flanges of the joint shown in Fig. 9.3 under horizontal bending, calculated by the finite element method. ['Zugspannungen' = 'tensile stress', 'Druckspannungen' = 'compressive stress', 'Profilaußenseite' = 'outside face', 'Querschnittsprofilscherpunkt' = 'centroid axis', 'Knotenbereich' = 'joint nodal area'.]

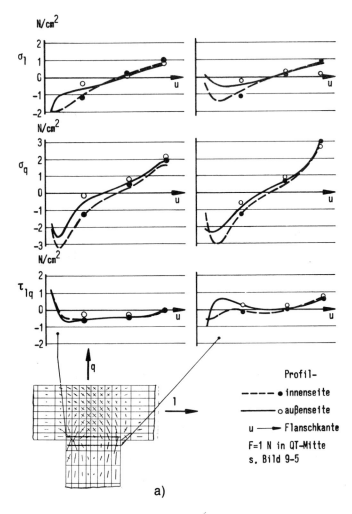

Fig. 9.6 Comparison of the measured and calculated stress distributions across the flanges of the joint of Fig. 9.5.
['Profil-innenseite' = 'inside face', 'Profile-außenseite' = 'outside face', 'Flanschkante' = 'edge of the flange', '*F* = 1 N in QT-mitte s. bild 9-5' = 'force *F* = 1 Newton at the centre of the cross member in Fig. 9.5', 'Verhältig Vergleichsspannung nach Huber–von Mises' = 'stresses reduced proportionally for the Huber-von Mises representation'.]

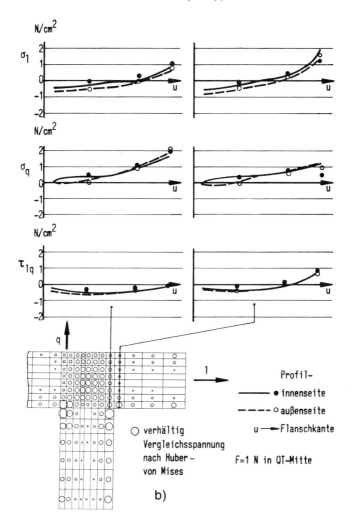

N/cm^2

σ_l

N/cm^2

σ_q

N/cm^2

τ_{lq}

q

l

Profil-

———— • innenseite

– – – – ○ außenseite

u ——► Flanschkante

○ verhältig
Vergleichsspannung
nach Huber –
von Mises

F=1 N in QT-Mitte

b)

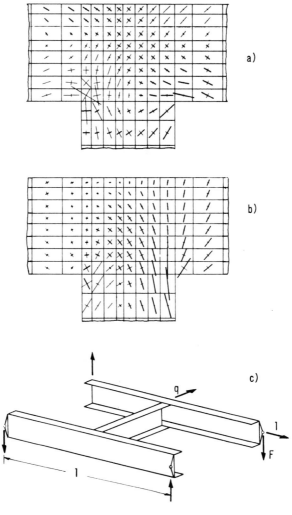

Fig. 9.7   Principal stresses in the flanges of the joint shown in Fig. 9.3 under torsion, calculated by the finite element method.
(a)   **Outside face**
(b)   **Inside face**

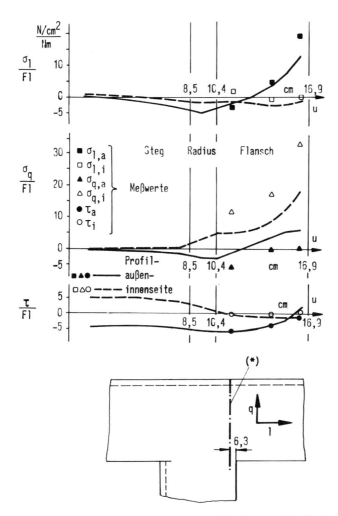

Fig. 9.8   **Comparison of the measured and calculated stress distributions across the side member at the cross section denoted by (*) and loaded as in Fig. 9.7.**
['Steg' = 'web'; 'Flansch' = 'flange'; 'Profil aussen' = 'outside face'; 'Profile innenseite' = 'inside face'.]

differences is deformation of the cross section, which results in stresses in the direction round the profile, or, when the deformation of the profile of the cross section is changing longitudinally, direct stresses in the longitudinal direction. Figure 9.7 shows the calculated principal stresses in the same simple joint when the section of the frame is subjected to torsion. As would be expected, large tensile stresses occur at the unsupported edges of the flanges, and this is also true to a lesser extent in the case of horizontal bending in the joint. For these reasons this type of joint is not commonly used in practice.

Figure 9.8 gives the comparison between the calculated stresses on the outside surface and the inside surface across the flange on the line denoted by (*). It can be seen that there is a considerable difference between the two distributions, particularly in the case of σ_q. Both the direct stresses show a difference between the internal and external values which is due to bending of the flange of the side member. The finite element analysis has not calculated the stress distribution at all accurately because the profile deformation at the boundaries of the substructure was too constrained by the supports. This has proved to be an important secondary effect in the analysis of nodal substructures and, as the example in Fig. 9.8 demonstrates, it is often necessary to check the analysis by experiment.

A more practical design of joint is shown in Figs 9.9 where the flanges of the side member and cross member channel sections are connected simply by flat plates. This type of joint is often used at the ends of the rear cross member, although in this example it is used in an 'H' section of a ladder frame consisting of only one cross member with half bay length side members. The principal stresses obtained from a finite element analysis are shown in the figures. By comparing the internal and external direct stresses it can be seen that there are pronounced bending stresses in the direction normal to the beam axes in the upper flanges and in the upper connecting plate. These are also due to the deformation of the cross section caused by the external loads. In this case it can be seen that the flange of the side member to the right of the node is being bent downwards. This means that the outside surface is in tension and the inside is in compression, and this stress distribution carries over into the connecting plate. These bending stresses arising from the torsion carried across the joint actually exceed the direct stresses due to the bimoment at the end of the cross member.

Measurements of the stress distribution in this type of joint have shown

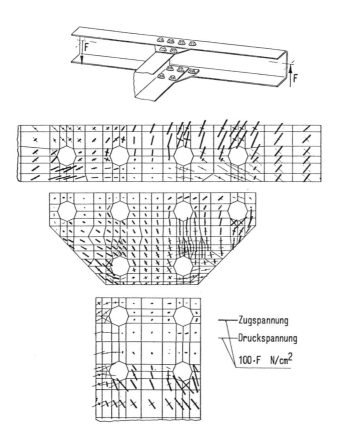

Fig. 9.9(a) Calculated principal stress distribution on the outside face of the upper flanges and gusset plate of a bolted joint with a gusset plate subject to torsion.
[Key gives length of line representing tensile and compression stresses equal to 100 N/cm²; 'Zugspannung' = 'tensile stress'; 'Druckspannung' = 'compression stress'.]

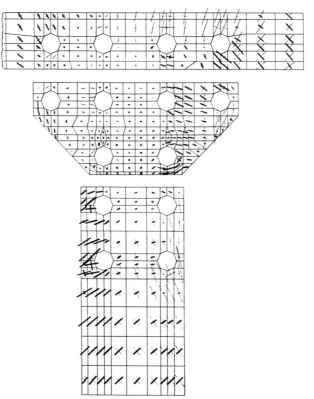

Fig. 9.9(b)   Calculated principal stress distribution on the inside face of the joint shown in Fig. 9.9(a)

that, when using two-dimensional elements, it is necessary to ensure equal displacements of the overlapping elements when they are pressed together. On the other hand, it is necessary to allow the elements in the flanges of the beams and in the plates to separate to obtain satisfactory agreement between theory and practice. This is shown in reference **(18)**, where 'gap' elements are used in a non-linear analysis.

Bolted and rivetted joints
A bolted joint is shown in Figs 9.9 where the bolts have been idealized as four eight noded three dimensional elements which fill the octagonal space in the finite element model. Figure 9.10 shows this idealization in

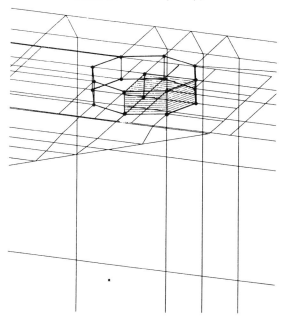

Fig. 9.10   Idealization used for the bolts in the analysis of Fig. 9.9, one of the eight noded three dimensional elements shown shaded

detail for one of the bolts between the side member flange and the gusset plate, with one of the elements shown shaded. The area of the octagon is equal to the effective cross sectional area of the bolt or rivet head. Even this idealization does not accurately represent the contact area between the two surfaces. One way to represent the effect of pressing the surfaces together is to assume that a single plate with a thickness equal to the sum of the two individual plates is effective over the overlapping area. This assumption can only be used in a flexibility analysis. If all the parts of a joint are idealized in this simple way the calculated joint flexibility will be too low. If only the octagonal bolt or rivet idealization is used, the joint flexibility will be too great. This implies that, with either assumption, it is to be expected that there will be a difference between the measured and calculated stress distributions.

10

Plate structures

In the stress analysis of chassis frames the theory of thin-walled beams as applied to matrix methods in chapter 7 should be used where possible, since the internal load–displacement relations are exact. The joints between the beam elements can only be analysed by non-computer methods in the case of very simple welded joints. In most cases, therefore, joints must be analysed by finite element methods involving flat plate elements, as shown in chapter 9. Such substructures are examples of small structures made up of plate elements.

It seems to be an obvious extension to the use of finite element methods to idealize the whole frame as a grid of small plate elements and use an available program system. Such systems typically make use of substructure techniques where they are advantageous. In these methods the displacement functions used for the plate elements in matrix displacement methods only approximate to the true internal displacements of the structure. The load–displacement relations within the structure are then found from the displacements, which means that they are necessarily more of an approximation than when the accurate internal stresses in the beam members are found by the thin-walled beam theory, and this is combined with simple finite element idealizations of the joints. This is confirmed by comparing the measured torsional stiffness of a chassis with the theoretical values obtained by the two methods. It should be remembered that finite element shape functions which ensure the compatibility of the element deformations include rigid body displacements and constant strains; these impose constraints on the calculated displacements of the structure and will always result in less deformation than the real structure. It is known, however, that a good approximation to the true value can be achieved even without using fully compatible elements, but without knowing whether the theoretical deformation is too large or too small.

In the case of commercial vehicle and bus structures, classical analytical methods are rarely used, although they do exist. Where possible the thin-walled beam theories derived in chapters 5 and 7 should be used as they not only give better results but also lead to a better understanding of the stress distribution in the structure and, therefore, better designs. In areas where it is not possible to use these theories the structure should be analysed by finite element methods involving plate elements. These areas occur at locations other than joints, e.g., variable cross section beams and special cross members which carry drive train components. These members can usually be dealt with using substructures, as discussed in chapter 9.

Structures which can be analysed by flat plate elements are found in many superstructures, e.g., bus bodies, cabs, load carrying bodywork, etc. Bus bodies have both glass and sheet metal panelling on a framework of tubing. It must be noted that the panels only carry significant load if the sheet metal is pre-stretched before fixing to the framework, which is usually the case due to the improved appearance it gives to the vehicle. The detailed finite element idealization of the whole structure depends on the program, together with the pre- and post-processors associated with it, so that the subject will not be pursued further in this book. However, the coarseness of the idealization to be used does depend on the purpose of the analysis. The deformation of a structure can normally be found adequately from a coarse mesh, and therefore, this is sufficient for dynamic analysis. This is because in the equation

$$\mathbf{M}\ddot{\mathbf{d}} + \mathbf{C}\dot{\mathbf{d}} + \mathbf{K}\mathbf{d} = \mathbf{f}(t) \qquad (1.3)$$

the stiffness matrix $\mathbf{K}$ depends more on the finite element mesh than does the mass matrix $\mathbf{M}$. The structural damping is normally low so that viscous damping can be used as a satisfactory approximation.

When a stress analysis is required, a finer mesh is needed for the finite element analysis, as shown in chapter 9. The fact that better results are obtained for stresses with a finer mesh of elements must not be taken to mean that exact analysis is always possible if a sufficiently fine mesh is used for any structure, although this opinion is often held. It was shown in chapter 9, in the case of joints in chassis frames, for example, that local plate bending due to tightening of bolts, or the effect of pressure between the plates, cannot be allowed for in simple finite element analysis, however fine the mesh. To allow for these effects properly would involve not only a finer mesh, but also the use of three-dimensional elements, algorithms to prevent interpenetration of the different parts, the friction between the plates, and the lifting of one plate from contact with another. Because of the complication of such an analysis only a combined experimental and analytical approach is realistic, where the theoretical part offers the chance to evaluate the effect of changing design variables rapidly and cheaply.

11

Combined stiffness of body and chassis

All vehicles with separate chassis have the bodywork or superstructure connected to the chassis frame by some form of body mounts. While the chassis frame may be assisted by the superstructure in bending, in torsion the superstructure is deformed by the flexing of the chassis frame, which causes stresses in the body structure. In order to avoid these stresses, flexible mounts are used, which result in additional degrees of freedom in the motion of the parts of the structure. In particular, stiff cabs have to be mounted on flexible chassis frames by elaborate spring/damper systems in order to achieve reasonable comfort for the driver. Simple rubber mounts do not allow sufficient travel or sophistication of dynamic design to give the required level of comfort.

As the load-carrying structures are normally fixed directly to the chassis frame, they have to be designed to allow considerable deformation in use. This requirement is well known in the case of platform bodies. Although these flat-platform load-carrying bodies are themselves very flexible in torsion, they stiffen the chassis frame more than would be expected from the sum of the two individual stiffnesses, because the torsion axes of the two substructures do not coincide. The torsional stiffness given by

$$c_T = \frac{M_D}{\varphi} \tag{11.1}$$

relates to the angle of twist, φ, between two cross sections at a distance, a, apart along the frame under a torque, M_D, between these two sections. Taking the case of a frame supported at three points, as in Fig. 11.1, it is clear that for a constant slope of the side member, α, the force required to create the twist at a distance a_2 from the fixed end would be smaller than that required at a distance a_1. The reduction in the force will be linear along the frame, as will be the increase in the angle of twist, φ. The torsional stiffness can then be expressed as

$$c_T = \frac{M_D}{\varphi} = \frac{Fb}{\varphi} \sim \frac{1}{a^2} \tag{11.2}$$

The twisting of the frame can be expressed in terms of the 'rate of twist'

110

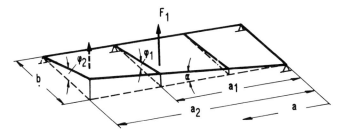

Fig. 11.1   Diagram for the notation for torsional stiffness and rate of twist stiffness

φ/a, when the corresponding 'force' will be $M_D a$, which has the dimensions of a bimoment. In this way the torsional behaviour of the frame can be expressed in terms of the rate of twist as

$$c_V = \frac{M_D a}{\varphi/a} = c_T a^2 \qquad (11.3)$$

where c_V is defined as the rate of twist stiffness of the frame.

This formula can be used immediately to find the combined torsional stiffness of two parallel structures. If the torsion axes coincided the combined rate of twist stiffness of a chassis frame and a load platform would be

$$c_{VR+P} = c_{VR} + c_{VP} \qquad (11.4)$$

where c_{VR} is the rate of twist stiffness of the chassis frame and c_{VP} the rate of twist stiffness of the platform body. The torsional stiffness can also be written in terms of the wheelbase, l, as

$$c_{TR+Pl} = \frac{c_{VR+P}}{l^2} = c_{TRl} + \frac{c_{VP}}{l^2} \qquad (11.5)$$

where c_{TRl} represents the torsional stiffness of the chassis frame related to the wheelbase. Tests on a platform truck showed that the wheelbase related torsional stiffness, c_{VP}/l^2, of the platform to be 12 per cent of the stiffness of the chassis with the cab. However, because the torsion axes do not coincide when the body is mounted on the chassis, the torsional stiffness is increased to 140 per cent of that of the chassis–cab. This increase in stiffness can be explained by reference to Fig. 11.2, where the horizontal forces acting on the chassis frame and the subframe of the body

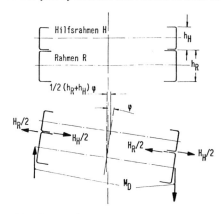

Fig. 11.2   Horizontal loads and displacements at the free end of a chassis and body subframe under torsion.
['Hilfsrahmen' means 'subframe', 'Rahmen' means 'chassis frame'.]

are shown. These are caused by the lateral bending deformation of the two frames causing the lateral displacement

$$\frac{(h_R + h_H)}{2}\varphi$$

Using the notation

$$c_B = \frac{Ha}{\gamma}$$

for the stiffness of the chassis frame in lateral bending, where the moment Ha arises from the horizontal force H acting in opposite directions at a distance a apart, and γ is the lateral shear angle caused by Ha. If the assumption is made that the chassis frame and the subframe are only connected at one end, the combined stiffness is given by

$$c_{VR+H} = c_{VR} + c_{VH} + 2\frac{c_{BR}c_{BH}}{c_{BR} + c_{BH}}\left(\frac{h_R + h_H}{2}\right)^2 \tag{11.6}$$

Equation (11.4) should also be enlarged to take account of the relative lateral bending, with the distance between the torsion axis of the platform and the flange of the frame supporting the platform used in place of $h_H/2$.

Equation (11.6) expresses the rule that 'the rate of twist stiffness of two

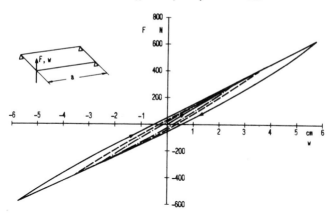

Fig. 11.3 **Load–displacement curves for a 5-bay frame under pure torsion showing hysteresis effect**

structures coupled in parallel is the sum of their individual rate of twist stiffnesses, plus the harmonic mean of the lateral bending stiffnesses multiplied by the square of the distance between their torsion axes'.

When bolted or rivetted joints are under very high stress they may be subject to slippage between the surfaces. This type of slipping results in a decreasing stiffness with increasing load, in other words a non-linear load–displacement relationship. Internal non-linearities of this type occur in commercial vehicles, both in the chassis frame joints themselves, and in the mounting points for subframes and superstructures, e.g., cabs, load-carrying bodywork, etc. As an example of the hysteresis caused by joints, Fig. 11.3 shows the displacement of the loading point of a commercial vehicle frame with rivetted joints under pure torsion. The displacement, w, is directly proportional to the angle of twist of the frame. (The rectangular frame drawn inset is only symbolic of the actual frame and is shown to illustrate the method of loading.) Considerably greater hysteresis has been measured in chassis frames with platform bodies attached.

12

The analysis of commercial vehicle chassis frames

The grillages normally used as chassis frames of commercial vehicles appear to be simple structures, which explains why they are frequently only analysed by equally simple methods. However, accurate analysis of load–deformation characteristics, and especially the analysis of stress distributions, are actually quite difficult. The treatment of the theoretical problems in chapters 5–9 suggest that experimental verification of calculations is only required if all the detailed structural properties are not to be ignored. Even rough estimates based on simplified assumptions are justified, however, when dimensions of the main members are required for preliminary design purposes.

12.1 SIMPLIFIED CALCULATIONS

The calculation is divided into the load cases described in chapter 3, as follows.

> Bending due to symmetrical vertical loads, braking and accelerating loads, and inertial loads due to bumps – i.e., vertical bending corresponding to load cases I, II, and V.

> Lateral bending arising from side forces, unsymmetrical longitudinal forces, scrubbing of non-steerable double axles – i.e., horizontal bending corresponding to load cases III and VII. Load case VI and the forces generated by the coupling of body and chassis also give rise to lateral bending.

> Torsion – corresponding to load case IV.

The case where horizontal bending and torsion arise together is not considered in this simplified calculation method.

Vertical bending
The chassis frames of two-axle vehicles and vehicles with balance-beam twin rear axles are treated as simply supported beams. The support loads from the axles are distributed through the spring hangers, as shown in

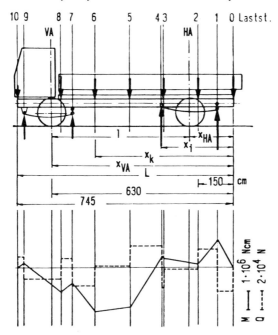

Fig. 12.1   Static loads, shear force diagram, and bending moment diagram for a truck under a simple dead load. Load case 1

Fig. 12.1. Double axles without a balancing mechanism result in a beam with redundant supports, and the distribution of the loads depends on the layout of the suspension.

For practical calculations it is recommended that the load on the chassis frame, including its own weight, is concentrated at a small number of points. These point loads are statically equivalent to the actual distributed load carried by the vehicle. In the case of the example in Fig. 12.1 the weight of the cab and the engine and gearbox are concentrated at the load points 8 and 10. The loads on the beam are represented in the shear force diagram shown in the figure. It is usual to work from the rear to the front when numbering the load points and plotting the shear force diagram, as the higher stresses occur at the rear of the chassis frame. The bending moment diagram can be plotted from the shear force diagram in the usual way. The bending moment at the load point i is

$$M_i = M_{i-1} + Q_{i-1}(x_i - x_{i-1})$$ (12.1)

where Q_{i-1} is the shear force at the point $i - 1$ and the distances x_1 and x_{i-1} are measured from the rear end.

As is well known, braking and acceleration cause pitching moments which have to be transferred to the frame as vertical loads through the spring hangers, the resulting bending moments act at the neutral axes of the frame side members. These bending moments are shown in Fig. 12.2. Initially, the masses representing the load and chassis frame are assumed to act at the level of the neutral axes of the side members resulting in the bending moment distribution shown dotted in Fig. 12.2, while the solid line represents the bending moment when the masses are assumed to act above the chassis frame, in this case 1.5 m above the road surface.

The extreme loads caused by bumps have already been discussed in chapter 3. As an example, the force A_{Hst} at the rear axle causes a vertical acceleration of the centre of gravity of the sprung mass m_2 which is given by

$$\ddot{z}_2 = \frac{A_{Hst}}{m_2}$$ (12.2)

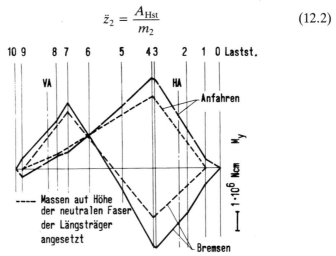

Fig. 12.2 **Bending moment diagrams for the truck in Fig. 12.1 under a braking deceleration of $a = 0.7$, and an acceleration corresponding to a maximum hill climbing ability of 40 per cent, load cases IIa and IIb. ['Lastst' means 'load point', 'Anfahren' means 'acceleration', 'Bremsen' means 'braking', 'Massen auf neutralen Faser der Längsträger angesetzt' means 'lumped masses assumed to be at the height of the side member neutral axis.**

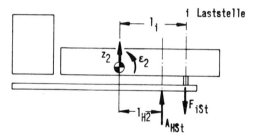

Fig. 12.3 Diagram for calculating the effect on the load at load point *i* of the rear axle hitting a bump

and the pitching acceleration about the lateral axis through the centre of gravity is

$$\ddot{\varepsilon}_2 = \frac{l_{H2}A_{HSt}}{\Theta_{2y}} \qquad (12.3)$$

where Θ_{2y} is the pitching moment of inertia of the sprung mass and the forces and dimensions are shown in Fig. 12.3. This approximation is sufficiently accurate because the change in the front spring force during the impact of the rear wheel with the bump is negligible. The increment of the force at load point i can then be written as

$$F_{iSt} = m_i(\ddot{z}_2 + l_i\ddot{\varepsilon}_2) \qquad (12.4)$$

or

$$F_{iSt} = m_i\left(\frac{1}{m_2} + \frac{l_{H2}l_i}{\Theta_{2y}}\right)A_{HSt} \qquad (12.5)$$

Figure 12.4 shows the bending moment diagrams for 100 per cent increase in the front axle load (dotted line) and in the rear axle load (full line). It can be seen by comparing the static bending moments from Fig. 12.1 with the dynamic bending moments in Fig. 12.4 that the dynamic bending moment over the rear axle is considerably greater when calculated in this way than if the usual method of factoring all the static loads is adopted.

Because the centre of gravity of the load is above the chassis frame the lateral acceleration due to cornering increases the load on the side member on the outside of the curve. This effect is illustrated in Fig. 12.5 where the lateral acceleration is taken as *a* times gravity, and the

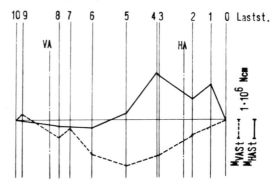

Fig. 12.4   Bending moment diagrams for the cases where the loads on the front and rear axles are increased by 100 per cent in turn. Load cases *Va* and *Vb*. ['Lastst' = 'load point'.]

increment in the force becomes $aF_i h_{si}/b$. It is sufficient to increase all the static loads on this side of the vehicle by the same factor. Unequal loads along the length of the vehicle will result in some torsion being applied to the frame, but, on the whole, this torque can be neglected.

The deflection of the frame is next in importance to the stresses and this can be found from the general formula in equation (4.2). Since the calculation of the deflection of a simply supported beam is well known it

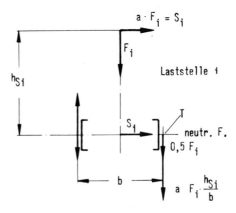

Fig. 12.5   Vertical loads at load point *i* during cornering with a lateral acceleration of *a*g

is better to consider the chassis frame as a beam on fictitious supports at the ends and then displace the deflected beam so that there is zero deflection at the axle centrelines. The influence coefficient, w_{ik}, is the deflection at load point i due to a unit load at load point k, i.e.

$$w_{ik} = \frac{1}{EJ_y} \frac{x_i(L - x_k)}{6L} \{L^2 - x_i^2 - (L - x_k)^2\} \tag{12.6}$$

This relation requires that $x_k > x_i$, but according to the Maxwell–Betti law for linear systems

$$w_{ik} = w_{ki} \tag{12.7}$$

The sagging deflection at load point i due to the loads F_1 to F_{n-1} is then

$$w_i = w_{i1}F_1 + w_{i2}F_2 \ldots w_{in-1}F_{n-1} \tag{12.8}$$

The influence coefficients can now be arranged in matrix form as

$$\mathbf{W} = \begin{bmatrix} w_{11} & w_{12} & \cdots & w_{1n-1} \\ w_{21} & & & \\ \vdots & & & \\ w_{n-11} & & & \end{bmatrix} \tag{12.9}$$

and the individual deflections can be written as a column matrix

$$\mathbf{w} = \{w_1 \ w_2 \ \ldots \ w_{n-1}\} \tag{12.10}$$

which is the result of the load column matrix

$$\mathbf{f} = \{F_1 \ F_2 \ \ldots \ F_{n-1}\}$$

so that

$$\mathbf{w} = \mathbf{Wf} \tag{12.11}$$

If the deflections at the front and rear axle centre lines are w_{VA} and w_{HA} respectively, then the total deflection of the load point i is

$$w_{Ai} = w_i - w_{HA} + \frac{w_{HA} - w_{VA}}{l}(x_i - x_{HA}) \tag{12.12}$$

For the example used in this section Fig. 12.6 shows the final deflection of the frame related to the line joining the axle support points.

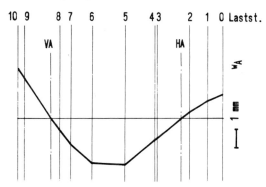

Fig. 12.6　Frame deflection for the static load case shown in Fig. 12.1

Horizontal bending

A ladder frame has, in general, an order of redundancy of $3(m-1)$ for m cross members. Since chassis frames are usually symmetrical this can be reduced to a single redundancy for each bay. This is shown in Fig. 12.7,

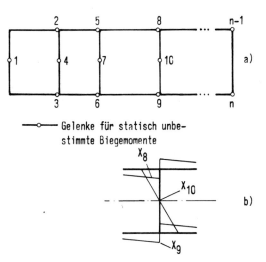

Fig. 12.7　(a)　Statically determinate basic system for horizontal bending
　　　　　　(b)　Redundant bending moments at one cross member and the adjoining side member elements
　　　　　　['Gelenke für statisch . . .', means 'points where redundant moments are introduced'.]

Fig. 12.7(a) gives the usual unknowns as numbered points, while Fig. 12.7(b) indicates that the unknown bending moments X_8 and X_9 are equal and that the bending moment at the centre of the cross members is zero, i.e., $X_{10} = 0$. Because there are normally only a small number of cross members in a chassis frame it is possible to analyse the frame by a classical method. This method does not take into account the flexibility of the joints as does the matrix force method in section 2 of this chapter. Since both methods give the internal loads in the basic system they can be used as a basis of comparison between the classical and matrix methods.

As an example, the frame of Fig. 12.1 is used with the lateral loads taken as half the vertical loads shown in that figure, in other words a cornering force of $\frac{1}{2}$ gravity. Figure 12.8(a) sets out the bending moment distribution in the basic system due to the external loads, called the M_0

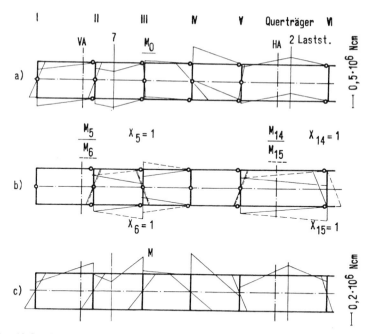

Fig. 12.8   Bending moments in the members of a frame in lateral bending.
(a)   In the basic system caused by a cornering load
(b)   Typical local distributions due to unit redundant load systems
(c)   Total bending moments due to load case III on the example shown in Fig. 12.1 (moments shown for one side member only)

distribution. The loads equivalent to the downward loads and the upward spring hanger loads in Fig. 12.1 are concentrated at the cross members I to VI and the load points 2 and 7. The frame is defined by the lines through the centroids of the cross members and side members.

The effect of the flexibility of the members themselves is included by defining unit unknown moments at the 'cuts' shown as pin joints in Figs 12.8(a) and (b). These unit moment redundant systems are shown as examples in Fig. 12.8(b) as M_5 caused by the unknown moment $X_5 = 1$ (solid line) and M_6 caused by the unknown moment $X_6 = 1$ (dotted line). The moment at the centre of the front cross member (No. I) is zero but the rear cross member (No. VI) has no cut at the centre so that the redundant systems, M_{14}, caused by the unknown moment $X_{14} = 1$, and M_{15}, caused by $X_{15} = 1$, define the bending in this cross member.

If there are n redundant systems, the total bending moment at any point is

$$M = M_0 + X_1 M_1 + X_2 M_2 + \ldots + X_n M_n \qquad (12.13)$$

where the true values of the redundancies are found by closing the cuts. In this case the displacements are rotations so that the relative angles of the ends of the beams at the joints must be zero. It is more practical, in this case, to use the principle of minimum strain energy rather than the usual compatibility condition to find the values of the redundancies. The internal strain energy is

$$W_{in} = \sum_h \int^{l_h} \frac{1}{2EJ_h} M^2 \, dl \qquad (12.14)$$

Since the direct and normal loads only make a small contribution to the strain energy they are ignored. The partial derivatives of the strain energy with respect to each of the redundancies in turn are equal to zero so that

$$\frac{\partial W_{in}}{\partial X_2} = 0; \quad \frac{\partial W_{in}}{\partial X_5} = 0; \quad \ldots; \quad \frac{\partial W_{in}}{\partial X_{n-1}} = 0 \qquad (12.15)$$

remembering that

$$X_1 = 0; \quad X_4 = 0; \quad \ldots$$
$$X_3 = X_2; \quad X_6 = X_5; \quad \ldots; \quad X_n = X_{n-1} \qquad (12.16)$$

The equations for the values of the unknown redundant moments can now be found.

The general equation for the moment at any point (12.13) can be written, using the relations of equation (12.16), as

$$M = M_0 + X_2(M_2 + M_3) + X_5(M_5 + M_6) + \ldots X_{n-1}(M_{n-1} + M_n)$$

and

$$M^2 = M_0^2 + X_2^2(M_2 + M_3)^2 + \ldots + X_{n-1}^2(M_{n-1} + M_n)^2$$
$$+ 2M_0X_2(M_2 + M_3) + \ldots$$
$$+ 2X_{n-4}(M_{n-4} + M_{n-3})X_{n-1}(M_{n-1} + M_n) \qquad (12.17)$$

The procedure is very much simplified when the partial derivatives are formed as in equation (12.15).

In order to find the internal energies, the integrals of equation (12.14) using the formula given in equation (12.17) have to be formed, so that for beam h, for instance

$$\int^{l_h} (M_2 + M_3)^2 \, dl$$

$$\int^{l_h} M_0(M_2 + M_3) \, dl$$

Table 12.1 gives a list of useful integrals to be used in these calculations. The moment distribution along the beams is usually triangular or rectangular as for the case of $M_2 + M_3$ and $M_5 + M_6$. Where an external load occurs in the bay area there will be a trapezium bending moment distribution. The final bending moment distribution over the whole frame is shown in Fig. 12.8(c).

When the matrix force method is used to analyse the frame the internal loads at the ends of the beams have to be entered into the $\mathbf{B}_0$ and $\mathbf{B}_1$ matrices in equation (4.21). The columns of $\mathbf{B}_0$ contain the internal loads at the ends of the beams for unit values of the external loads in turn, and zero values of the redundant loads. The matrix $\mathbf{B}_1$ contains the internal loads due to unit values of the redundant loads, each column is due to one redundancy and the terms are as in equation (4.15). Parts of the flexibility matrix, equation (4.16a), corresponding to the displacements u_h, β_{z1h}, β_{z2h} and the loads N_h, M_{z1h}, M_{z2h}, can be arranged diagonally to form a new flexibility matrix $\mathbf{F}_v$ as in equation (4.17).

The compatibility conditions, expressed in equation (4.32), then give the values of the unknown redundant loads $\mathbf{X}$ due to external unit loads.

Table 12.1   Integrals of the products of bending moments for standard member bending moment diagrams

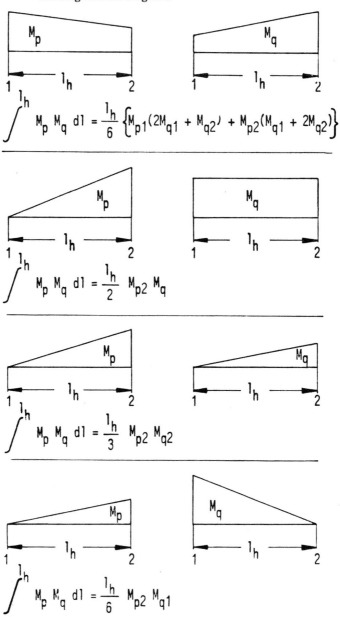

$$\int^{l_h} M_p\, M_q\, dl = \frac{l_h}{6}\left\{M_{p1}(2M_{q1} + M_{q2}) + M_{p2}(M_{q1} + 2M_{q2})\right\}$$

$$\int^{l_h} M_p\, M_q\, dl = \frac{l_h}{2}\, M_{p2}\, M_q$$

$$\int^{l_h} M_p\, M_q\, dl = \frac{l_h}{3}\, M_{p2}\, M_{q2}$$

$$\int^{l_h} M_p\, M_q\, dl = \frac{l_h}{6}\, M_{p2}\, M_{q1}$$

Finally the internal loads at the ends of the beams are obtained as the column vector, **p**, equation (4.19), by the use of equation

$$\mathbf{p} = (\mathbf{B}_0 + \mathbf{B}_1\mathbf{X})\mathbf{f}_F \qquad (4.24)$$

The stress distribution at any cross section of the beams making up the frame can now be found from these internal loads.

Further manipulation of the results of the analysis of the basic system will be necessary for both the classical and matrix force methods. Such manipulation is much more systematic when using the matrix force method in a computer program. The advantages in this method can be seen when the flexibility of the joints is included in the analysis, as in section 2 of this chapter.

The example in Fig. 12.8 relates to a vehicle in a steady cornering state, load case III. The case when the vehicle is subjected to an asymmetrical longitudinal force, load case VII, is shown as a basic system in Fig. 12.9. The internal load distributions in the redundant systems remain the same so that only the terms not containing X in equation (12.15) and the partial derivatives of M^2 are changed.

The final in-plane stressing case to be considered is the towing case, which imposes a bending moment, M_K, at the centre of the rear cross member, and a moment, M_L, at the rear end of the side members, as shown in Fig. 12.10. Although these moments are only approximate they are sufficiently accurate to be used as a single redundant system. The values of the moments are

$$M_K = \frac{(l_{m-1}/b) + 3/4(J_L/J_{SQ})}{(l_{m-1}/b) + 3/2(J_L/J_{SQ})} \cdot \frac{bD}{4} \qquad (12.18)$$

$$M_L = \frac{bD}{4} - M_K \qquad (12.19)$$

where J_L and J_{SQ} are the second moments of area of the side member and the cross member, respectively. The first term of equation (12.18)

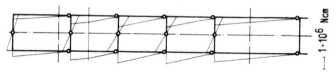

Fig. 12.9 Bending moments in the basic system of the frame of the example in Fig. 12.1 due to a longitudinal load on one side

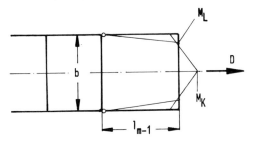

Fig. 12.10   Bending moment distribution in the end bay due to a towing force D, load case VI

represents the reduction of the bending moment at the centre of the rear cross member due to the effect of rigid joints at the ends of this cross member.

The towing force is given by

$$D = \frac{m_Z m_A}{m_Z m_A} \qquad (12.20)$$

where m_z is the mass of the truck and m_A the mass of the trailer. It is assumed that one of the two vehicles is unbraked and decelerated by the other. Equation (12.20) includes a dynamic safety factor which is equal to the reciprocal of the actual deceleration of the braked vehicle, so that the deceleration is effectively 1 g.

Torsion
The torque on the chassis frame to be used as a stressing case depends on the torsional stiffness of the suspension and the torsional stiffness of the frame itself. The torque is found by specifying the height of a bump on which one of the wheels rests while the other three wheels are on level ground. This condition is illustrated in Fig. 12.11, where h_{Rd} is the height of the bump, and the spring rates and the relevant dimensions are shown. The angle of twist between the axle centre lines is taken as φ_R, and the torsional stiffness of the frame between the axles is c_{TR}. The moment acting on the frame is then

$$M_R = \frac{h_{Rd}}{s_V} \bigg/ \left(\frac{2}{s_V^2 c_{1V}} + \frac{2}{s_{FV}^2 c_{2V}} + \frac{2}{s_{FH}^2 c_{2H}} + \frac{2}{s_H^2 c_{1H}} + \frac{1}{c_{TR}} \right) \qquad (12.21)$$

It should be noted that the small angle approximation $\sin \varphi \approx \varphi$ is made

Vorderachse   Hinterachse

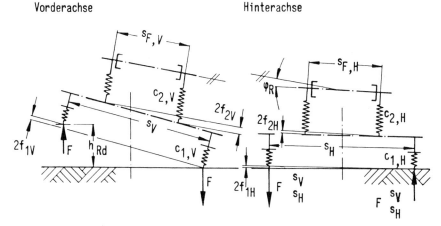

Fig. 12.11   Axle and frame positions when one wheel is on a bump, angle of twist of frame φ_R. ['Vorderachse' = 'front axle'; 'Hinterachse' = 'rear axle'.]

in this calculation. Any added structure will increase the torsional stiffness of the frame and also the torsion load or torque it will carry.

As described in chapter 3, the maximum torque that can be applied to the vehicle with a stiff chassis frame and a front axle load of P_v is

$$P_v s_v$$

A ladder frame with m cross members in torsion has an order of redundancy of $3(m - 1)$. Because of symmetry there will be equal torques in the two side members and, therefore, there will be zero bending moments at the centre of the cross members. The frame can be idealized with longitudinal hinges at the centres of the cross members, and this reduces the order of redundancy to two per bay. Figure 12.12 shows the

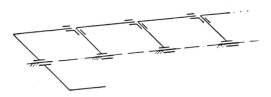

Fig. 12.12   Statically determinate basic system for torsional analysis of a frame

basic system used for the analysis of the frame. The details of the matrix force method used, which can include the effect of joint flexibility, are given in section 12.2.

Commercial vehicle chassis frames are generally made with open section side and cross members, and these are very torsionally flexible; the so called 'torsionally soft' chassis. For these frames the beam elements, which are the cross members and the parts of the side members between the cross members, can be considered to remain straight under torsion, and defined by their torsion centre axes, as in Fig. 12.13. The angle of twist and the rate of twist of each element can now be found from the figure. For the side members it is

$$\frac{w}{b/2} \quad \text{and} \quad \vartheta_\text{L} = 2\,\frac{w}{bl} \qquad (12.22a)$$

and for the cross members

$$2\,\frac{w}{l} \quad \text{and} \quad \vartheta_\text{Q} = 2\,\frac{w}{bl} \qquad (12.22b)$$

These formulae can be used in the approximate method of analysis given by Erz in reference (5).

Since

$$M_\text{D} = GJ_\text{t}\vartheta \qquad (12.23)$$

the torques in the elements of the frame are proportional to their torsion constants, J_t, as the rate of twist is the same, see equations (12.22). Thus, when the torque in one beam element is known, the torques in the others can be found from their torsion constants.

The torques in the side member elements cause bending moments in

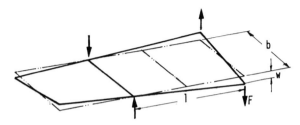

Fig. 12.13   Torsional deformation of a torsionally soft frame to show the connection between the linear displacements and the torsion angle

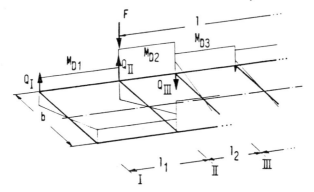

Fig. 12.14 Normal forces at the joints of the side members caused by the bending moments in the cross members which also cause the changes in the torque along the side member at each joint

the cross members which again cause normal internal loads, Q, at the joints. This effect is illustrated in Fig. 12.14 for cross members I, II, and III, resulting in the equations

$$Q_\mathrm{I} = M_\mathrm{D1} \frac{2}{b} \tag{12.24a}$$

$$Q_\mathrm{II} = (M_\mathrm{D2} - M_\mathrm{D1}) \frac{2}{b} \tag{12.24b}$$

$$Q_\mathrm{III} = (M_\mathrm{D3} - M_\mathrm{D2}) \frac{2}{b} \tag{12.24c}$$

similar equations can also be written for all the other cross members.

The bending moments in the side members are due to the torques in the cross members, $M_\mathrm{DI}-M_\mathrm{Dm}$, the longitudinal moments from the normal internal loads, Q, and the four forces, F, comprising the external torque. The equilibrium of moments at the front of the side member can be expressed as

$$F \cdot l - (M_\mathrm{DI} + M_\mathrm{DII} + \ldots + M_\mathrm{Dm}) + Q_\mathrm{II} l_1 + Q_\mathrm{III}(l_1 + l_2) + \ldots$$
$$+ Q_\mathrm{m}(l_1 + l_2 + \ldots + l_{m-1}) = 0 \tag{12.25}$$

From equation (12.23) the torques in all the beam elements can be expressed in terms of the torque in the front cross member as

$$M_{\text{DII}} = \frac{J_{\text{tll}}^*}{J_{\text{tl}}^*} M_{\text{DI}}$$

$$\cdot$$
$$\cdot$$
$$\cdot$$

$$M_{\text{DI}} = \frac{J_{\text{tl}}^*}{J_{\text{tl}}^*} M_{\text{DI}} \qquad (12.26)$$

$$\cdot$$
$$\cdot$$
$$\cdot$$

$$M_{\text{Dm}-1} = \frac{J_{\text{tm}-1}^*}{J_{\text{tl}}^*} M_{\text{DI}}$$

after the values of the internal normal loads have been substituted from equations (12.24); and since $M_{\text{R}} = Fb$

$$M_{\text{DI}} = \frac{M_{\text{R}}(l/b)J_{\text{tl}}^*}{\sum\limits_{h=1}^{m} J_{\text{th}}^* + (2/b) \sum\limits_{h=1}^{m-1} (J_{\text{th}}^* l_h)} \qquad (12.27)$$

Erz, (5), assumed that there is complete inhibition of warping in the joints of the chassis frame so that the effective torsion constants J_t^*, previously defined in equation (7.1), can be used for beam h as

$$J_{\text{th}}^* = J_{\text{th}} \frac{(\alpha_h l_h/2)}{(\alpha_h l_h/2) - \tanh (\alpha_h l_h/2)} \qquad (12.28)$$

where J_{th} is the St Venant torsion constant defined for open sections in equation (5.16) and the warping constant α is defined in equation (5.29).

The deflection of the frame in torsion and consequently the torsional stiffness is found by equating the internal and external work

$$\tfrac{1}{2}M_{\text{R}}\varphi_{\text{R}} = \tfrac{1}{2}\sum_{h} M_{\text{Dh}}\varphi_h \qquad (12.29)$$

where

$$\varphi_h = \frac{M_{\text{Dh}}}{GJ_{\text{th}}^*} l_h$$

$$M_{\text{R}}\varphi_{\text{R}} = \frac{1}{G} \sum_{h} \frac{M_{\text{Dh}}^2}{J_{\text{th}}^*} l_h \qquad (12.30)$$

so that the stiffness is

$$c_{TR} = \frac{M_R}{\varphi_R}$$

$$c_{TR} = G \bigg/ \sum_h \frac{(M_{Dh}/M_R)^2}{J^*_{th}} \, l_h \qquad (12.31)$$

The torque in each beam element as a fraction of the torque on the whole frame, M_{Dh}/M_R, is found by first putting $M_R = 1$. The actual torque on the frame is given by equation (12.21) and the torque in each beam element is then found from equations (12.26) and (12.27). The bending moments in the beams are found from the equilibrium conditions at the joints. Figure 12.15 gives the final torque and bending moment distribution for the frame used as an example in pure torsion.

So far the bimoment stresses have not been included, although the effect of warping inhibition has been taken into account in calculating the internal loads. These can be added separately as an approximation. When warping is completely inhibited at both ends of the beam the bimoments at the ends are equal and opposite. Equation (5.31c) with $\varphi_0' = 0$ and $B(l/2) = 0$ gives the bimoment at the end of the beam as

$$B_0 = \frac{1}{\alpha} \tanh \frac{\alpha l}{2} \cdot M_D \qquad (12.32)$$

and equations (5.23) and (5.29) give

$$\sigma_x = \frac{\omega}{\alpha J_\omega} \tanh \frac{\alpha l}{2} \cdot M_D \qquad (12.33)$$

which may be used to give a rough approximation to the stresses due to warping inhibition.

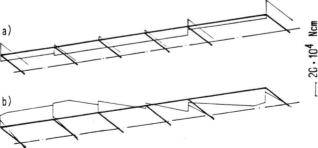

Fig. 12.15 Distribution of (a) the torques, and (b) the bending moments of the frame shown in Fig. 12.1 for load case IV. Warping assumed to be zero at the ends of the beams.

12.2 TORSIONAL ANALYSIS INCLUDING WARPING AND JOINT FLEXIBILITY

The simplified calculation explained in section 1 of this chapter assumed that the warping of the beam elements was completely inhibited, whereas they are actually only subject to partial warping inhibition. Also, the method of calculating the joint flexibilities given in chapter 8, section 8.2 was ignored. If the analytical results are to approach the experimental figures, both of these effects must be included. To achieve this the matrix methods of analysis described in chapter 4, sections 4.2 and 4.3 should be used.

12.2.1 Effect of warping of beam cross sections

Chapters 5 and 6 show that the stress distribution in the cross section of a thin-walled beam can be divided into seven internal load systems. The seventh, resulting from warping, is the bimoment, with the rate of twist as the corresponding displacement. The transfer of bimoments across joints is not statically determinate, as shown in chapter 8.2, and the method of illustrating this is shown in Fig. 8.7. The bimoments of Fig. 8.8 required to close the cuts shown in Fig. 8.6 are found from the compatibility of the rate of twist at the joint. The frame idealization shown in Fig. 12.12 has to be enlarged to include the zero warping axes, whose intersections are the points where the bimoments are transferred, to give the diagram shown in Fig. 12.16. The unknown bimoments, X_1, X_4, X_5, X_8, X_9, etc., are added to the unknown moments, X_2, X_3, X_6, X_7, etc. There is only one unknown bimoment at each end of the front and rear cross members, while there are two unknown bimoments at the ends of each of the other cross members. As shown in chapter 8, section 8.2, the bimoments are transferred across the joint at the intersection of the zero warping axes. It has been proved that the lengths of the side-member beam elements can be defined with sufficient accuracy by the distances between the intersections of the zero warping axes, l_{L2}, l_{L4}, etc., rather than the distances between the intersections of the torsion centre axes, l_2, l_4, as shown in Fig. 12.16.

Flexibility matrices of beam elements

The flexibility matrices for open-section thin-walled beam elements follow from the flexibility matrix in equation (7.5). The general displacement and load column matrices of equations (7.3) and (7.4) are reduced

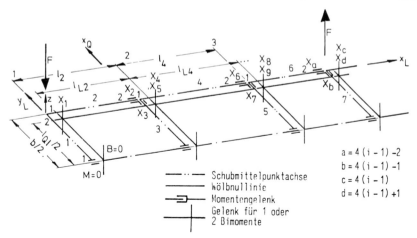

$$a = 4(i-1)-2$$
$$b = 4(i-1)-1$$
$$c = 4(i-1)$$
$$d = 4(i-1)+1$$

————··—— Schubmittelpunktachse
—————— Wölbnullinie
——⊐—— Momentengelenk
———— Gelenk für 1 oder
        2 Bimomente

Fig. 12.16   Basic system for a ladder frame including warping effects.
Schubmittelpunktachse = torsion centre axes
Wölbnullinie = zero warping axes
Momentengelenk = moment hinge (joint with zero moment)
Gelenk für 1 oder 2 Bimomente = hinge for 1 or 2 bimoments

for grillages by omitting the elements relating to in-plane bending, so that
they become

$$\mathbf{v}_{Lh} = \{\beta_{y1h} \; \beta_{y2h} \; \varphi_h \; \varphi'_{1h} \; \varphi'_{2h}\} \tag{12.34}$$

and

$$\mathbf{p}_{Lh} = \{M_{y1h} \; M_{y2h} \; M_{Dh} \; B_{1h} \; B_{2h}\} \tag{12.35}$$

and the flexibility matrix becomes as shown in (12.36) overleaf where the
suffix 'h' has been left out of the terms l_{Lh}, α_h, ψ_h, and η_h and

$$\psi = EJ_y \tag{12.37}$$

where J_y is substituted for J.

Also $\eta = GJ_t$, as in equation (5.30), and α is the warping constant
defined in equation (5.29). The cross sectional data for each of the beams
is also required.

The frame is defined by the lines representing the torsion centre axes,
but the bending moment at the end of a cross member is transferred at the

$$\mathbf{F}_{\text{Lh}} = \begin{bmatrix} \dfrac{l_L}{3\psi} & -\dfrac{l_L}{6\psi} & & & \\[2mm] -\dfrac{l_L}{3\psi} & \dfrac{l_L}{3\psi} & & & \\[2mm] & & \dfrac{l_L}{\eta} & \dfrac{1}{\eta} & \dfrac{1}{\eta} \\[2mm] & & \dfrac{1}{\eta} & \dfrac{\alpha}{\eta}\coth \alpha l_L & \dfrac{\alpha}{\eta}\dfrac{1}{\sinh \alpha l_L} \\[2mm] & & \dfrac{1}{\eta} & \dfrac{\alpha}{\eta}\dfrac{1}{\sinh \alpha l_L} & \dfrac{\alpha}{\eta}\coth \alpha l_L \end{bmatrix}$$

(12.36)

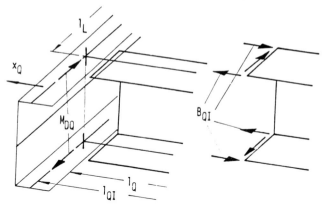

Fig. 12.17   Bimoment induced when the torque is not transferred at the end of the beam

bimoment joint, i.e., the intersection of the zero warping axes, Fig. 8.7. The actual length of the cross member is l_Q, and the bending slope at the end of cross member becomes

$$\beta_{2Q} = \frac{l_Q/2}{3\psi}\,\frac{l_Q^2}{bl_{QI}}\,M_{2Q} \tag{12.38}$$

A torque introduced into the cross member at the intersection of the zero warping lines shown in Fig. 8.7 can be resolved into a moment and a bimoment at the end of the cross member as illustrated in Fig. 12.17, giving the equation

$$B_{QI} = \frac{l_{QI} - l_Q}{2}\,M_{DQ} \tag{12.39}$$

This bimoment increases linearly from zero at the intersection of the zero warping lines to B_{QI} at the end of the beam. It can be seen in Fig. 12.17 that if the torque M_D is positive the distance from the intersection of the zero warping lines to the end of the beam is in the negative x direction, so that the rate of change of the bimoment with x is negative and becomes

$$B' = \frac{B_{QI}}{(l_{QI} - l_Q)/2} \tag{12.40}$$

and, since equation (5.24) shows that the torque due to warping is equal to minus the rate of change of bimoment

$$M_D = -B' = \frac{B_{QI}}{(l_{QI} - l_Q)/2}$$

as in equation (12.39).

The angle of twist of the cross member between the bimoment joints is

$$\varphi_{QI} = \varphi_Q + \varphi_Q'(l_{QI} - l_Q) \qquad (12.41)$$

The angle of twist φ_Q between the ends of the cross member due to the torque M_D and the bimoment B_{QI} is given by

$$\varphi_Q = \frac{l_Q}{\eta} M_{DQ} + \frac{2}{\eta} B_{QI} \qquad (12.42)$$

The relations given in (5.31) are used to obtain the second term. These relations also give the second term in the equation for φ_Q'

$$\varphi_Q' = \frac{1}{\eta} M_{DQ} + \frac{1}{\eta} \frac{1 + \cosh \alpha l_Q}{(1/\alpha) \sinh \alpha l_Q} B_{QI} \qquad (12.43)$$

For the length of the cross member between the bimoment joints the coefficient

$$\eta_{QI} = \frac{M_{DQ}}{\varphi_{QI}/l_{QI}}$$

can be written, by using the definition of B_{QI} in equation (12.39) and after some derivation, as

$$\eta_{QI} = \eta \left[l_{QI} \middle/ \left\{ 2l_{QI} - l_Q + \alpha \frac{1 + \cosh \alpha l_Q}{\sinh \alpha l_Q} \frac{(l_{QI} - l_Q)^2}{2} \right\} \right] \qquad (12.44)$$

Finally the angle of twist φ_{QI} due to the bimoment B_2 acting on the cross member follows from equations (5.31) as

$$\varphi_{QI} = \frac{1}{\eta} \left(1 + \alpha \frac{l_{QI} - l_Q}{2} \coth \alpha \frac{l_Q}{2} \right) B_2 \qquad (12.45)$$

remembering that $B(l_Q/2) = 0$. Since both the bending moment and the bimoment are zero at the centre of the cross member the displacements and loads required reduce to

$$\mathbf{v}_{Qh} = \{\beta_{y2h} \ \varphi_h \ \varphi_{2h}'\} \qquad (12.46)$$

and

$$\mathbf{p}_{Qh} = \{M_{y2h} \;\; M_{Dh} \;\; B_{2h}\} \tag{12.47}$$

The flexibility matrix for the cross member now becomes

$$\mathbf{F}_{Qh} = \begin{bmatrix} \dfrac{l_Q/2}{3\psi}\dfrac{l_Q^2}{bl_{QI}} & & \\[2ex] & \dfrac{l_{QI}/2}{\eta_{QI}} & \dfrac{1}{\eta}\left(1 + \alpha\,\dfrac{l_{QI} - l_Q}{2}\coth\alpha\,\dfrac{l_Q}{2}\right) \\[3ex] & \dfrac{1}{\eta}\left(1 + \alpha\,\dfrac{l_{QI} - l_Q}{2}\coth\alpha\,\dfrac{l_Q}{2}\right) & \dfrac{\alpha}{\eta}\coth\alpha\,\dfrac{l_Q}{2} \end{bmatrix}$$

$$\tag{12.48}$$

where the subscript 'h' is omitted from l_{Qh}, l_{QIh}, α_h, ψ_h and η_h.

Closed section thin walled beam cross members are only used occasionally in chassis frame designs, but again a simplified method of analysis can be used ignoring the deformation of the profile of the section. Since the bending moment and the bimoment are also zero at the centre of the cross member in this case the displacement and load column vectors are

$$\mathbf{v}_{Qh} = \{\beta_{y2h} \;\; \varphi_h \;\; W_{2h}\} \tag{12.49}$$

$$\mathbf{p}_{Qh} = \{M_{y2h} \;\; M_{Dh} \;\; B_{2h}\} \tag{12.50}$$

The warping displacement, W, is given in general terms by equations (6.1) and (6.2). The compatibility at the joint depends on the rate of twist φ' so that, using the relationships given in equation (6.35), the flexibility matrix becomes

$$\mathbf{F}_{Qt}^{closed} = \begin{bmatrix} \dfrac{l_Q^3}{6\psi bl_{QSt}} & & \\[2ex] & \dfrac{l_Q^3}{2Ea_1 k^2} & -\dfrac{a_3 l_Q^3}{Ea_1 a_2 k^2} \\[3ex] & -\dfrac{a_3 l_Q^2}{Ea_1 a_2 k^2} & \dfrac{l_Q}{Ea_1 k}\coth\dfrac{k}{2} \end{bmatrix} \tag{12.51}$$

Again the subscript 'h' is omitted from l_{Qh}, l_{QSth}, ψ_h, a_{1h}, a_{2h}, a_{3h}, and k_h. The parameters a_1, a_2, a_3, and k are given in equations (6.19) and (6.36).

Because of the shear deformation described in chapter 6 it is not possible to locate the position of the point where the bimoment is transferred at the intersection of the zero warping lines. This point has to be located at the web of the side member so that l_{QSt} is the length of the cross member between the webs of the side members.

In the case of a square section box beam cross member $a_3 = 0$ and F_{Qh}^{closed} is a diagonal matrix. There is no warping in square-section thin-walled beams so that a bimoment at the end does not cause twisting of the beam.

The profile deformation can also be taken as zero at the ends of the cross member for most practical designs of joint between the cross member and side member, so no additional internal load or displacement systems are needed in the analysis. When a more accurate analysis is required, the slightly more elaborate flexibility matrix given in reference (4) can be used together with the 4 × 4 matrices for the profile deformation at the ends of the cross member. The results from the two methods of analysis were compared with each other and with experiment for two-bay frames. The comparison showed that the more elaborate analysis gave only slightly better agreement with the test result.

Matrix analysis of chassis frames
When the matrix force method is used the procedure given in chapter 4, section 4.2, can be followed with the beam element flexibility matrices arranged on the main diagonal of the F_v matrix in the order shown in Fig. 12.16.

$$F_v = \begin{bmatrix} F_{Q1} & & & & \\ & F_{L2} & & & \\ & & F_{Q3} & & \\ & & & F_{L4} & \\ & & & & \ddots \end{bmatrix} \qquad (12.52)$$

The B_0 and B_1 matrices are the internal loads at the beam ends due to unit values of the external load and the redundant forces respectively. The latter become $X_i = 1$ for all X.

The statically indeterminate bimoments between the side member and cross member and between the side member elements at joint 2 of the frame illustrated in Fig. 12.16 are shown in Fig. 12.18. These consist of the bimoments between the cross member, beam 3, and the side member,

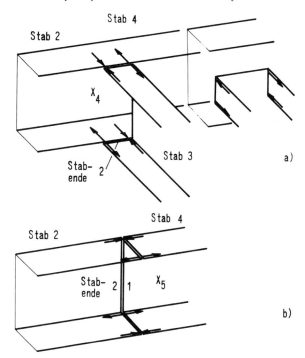

Fig. 12.18   Statically indeterminate bimoments:
  (a)   between side member and cross member for both vertical and horizontal cross member webs
  (b)   between side member sections, as in joint 2 of the example shown in Fig. 12.16

beam 2, in Fig. 12.18(a), and the two side member beam elements, 2 and 4, in Fig. 12.18(b). The way a bimoment closes 'cuts' was illustrated in Fig. 8.8 and the transfer of a bimoment to a side member was illustrated in Fig. 5.7. The sign of the bimoment acting on a cross member depends on the orientation of the channel section of the cross member, as was demonstrated in chapter 5. It can be seen from Fig. 12.18(a) with the help of Fig. 5.1 that the four forces acting on the end of the cross member with a vertical web result in a positive bimoment, but those acting on the cross member horizontal web give a negative bimoment.

Table 12.2 gives the matrices required for the matrix force method in

The analysis of commercial vehicle structures

Table 12.2 Matrices B_0 and B_1 for ladder frames with m cross members. (Lower signs apply to cross members with horizontal webs.)

Stabend-kräfte	durch F $=1$	X_1 $=1$	X_2 $=1$	X_3 $=1$	X_4 $=1$	X_5 $=1$	$\cdots$	$X_{4(m-1)}$ $=1$
M_{21}			$-1_{QI}/b$					
M_{D1}	-1_2		$1_2/\frac{b}{2}$	-1				
B_{21}		± 1						
M_{12}	1_2		$-1_2/\frac{b}{2}$	1				
M_{22}				-1				
M_{D2}				1				
B_{12}		-1						
B_{22}					-1	1		
M_{23}			$1_{QI}/b$					
M_{D3}	-1_4				1			
B_{23}						± 1		
M_{14}	1_4							
M_{24}								
M_{D4}								
B_{14}						-1		
$\vdots$							$\ddots$	
$B_{2\,\ell(m-1)}$								-1
$M_{2\,\ell(m-1)+1}$								
$M_{D\,2(m-1)+1}$								
$B_{2\,2(m-1)+1}$								± 1
p	**B_0**							**B_1**

(Untere Vorzeichen bei liegenden Querträgern)

detail with the column matrix **p** containing all the internal loads in the frame elements. $\mathbf{B}_0$ is the column matrix of internal loads due to a unit value of the external force F which applies the torque to the frame. This torque is applied to the frame by four forces F, two of these are illustrated in Fig. 12.16, one of these two forces is a reaction at a pin jointed support. The columns X_2–X_5 in the $\mathbf{B}_1$ matrix are the internal loads corresponding to unit values of the unknown redundancies X at one joint. This is repeated at each joint except for the front and rear cross member joints, i.e., from X_2 to X_5 at cross member 2 and from $X_{4(i-1)-2}$ to $X_{4(i-1)+1}$ at the ith cross member, where the notation is given in Fig. 12.16. The $\mathbf{B}_0$ and $\mathbf{B}_1$ matrices for frames with closed section cross members are given in reference (4). The two cases of these slightly more elaborate matrices, namely, with and without the effect of the deformation of the profile, are given in that reference.

The analysis can then be carried out as in chapter 4, section 4.2, with the values of the redundancies, $\mathbf{X}$, found from equation (4.32) and the internal loads from equation (4.24). The displacement in the direction of the force F is obtained from equation (4.33) when $\mathbf{F}_F$ has been found from equation (4.35). Note that $\mathbf{F}_F$ is a scalar in this case. The twist and torsional stiffness of the frame come from the vertical displacement of the corner, as indicated in Fig. 11.1, and the applied torque as in equation (11.3).

The matrix displacement method can also be used to analyse a chassis frame as set out in chapter 4, section 4.3. In this method the cross member stiffness matrix has to be transformed, as in equation (8.7), in order to maintain compatibility at the joints. The transfer matrix $\mathbf{T}_d$ written out in detail in equation (8.11) can be used for one end of the beam element comprising a cross member when only half the frame is analysed because of symmetry. If the symmetry condition cannot be used, each cross member has two $\mathbf{T}_d$ matrices on the main diagonal. The signs of the elements in the transfer matrices are found from Fig. 8.5. Here the beam-element stiffness matrix from equation (7.12) is used which contains lateral stiffness terms as well as torsional stiffness terms. The coupling of these two modes of deflection will be dealt with in section 12.3.

The beam elements have been represented in this section by their centroid axes, as in chapter 8.1, and the lengths by the distances between the intersections of these axes. The external forces, F, however, have to be introduced at the torsion centres of the side members.

12.2.2   Rate of twist flexibility of joints

The parameter δ_{LQF} was introduced to represent the rate of twist flexibility of a joint. It was calculated by the use of a finite element method. The terms in the compatibility equation

$$\mathbf{B_1^T F_v B_0} + \mathbf{B_1^T F_v B_1 X} = 0 \qquad (4.32)$$

can be interpreted as representing the 'cuts' in the joint which are sufficient to give a basic system. The first term representing the gaps in the basic system for unit external loads, and the second term the changes in these gaps due to the values of the redundant loads, $\mathbf{X}$, for unit external loads, see equation (4.23). If one nodal flexibility matrix, $\mathbf{D_F}$, is added, the compatibility equation can be enlarged to

$$\mathbf{B_1^T F_v B_0} + (\mathbf{B_1^T F_v B_1} + \mathbf{D_F})\mathbf{X} = 0 \qquad (12.53)$$

Nodal flexibilities are placed on the diagonal of the matrix, $\mathbf{D_F}$. In this way the deformation of the nodes are included when the gaps are closed by the redundant X forces. The columns of $\mathbf{X}$ are arranged in the order shown in Fig. 12.16. Since there is only one external torque in that figure, $\mathbf{X}$ is a column matrix. In this case X_1 is an unknown redundant bimoment, as are X_4, X_5, X_8, X_9, etc. Since the side member beam elements 2 and 4 are rigidly connected – usually they are two sections of the same side member – the bimoment redundancy, X_5, has zero flexibility associated with it. This is illustrated in Fig. 12.18(b). The rate of twist flexibilities of the intersections of the cross members with the side members are given by the cuts equivalent to X_1, X_4, ... These can be generalized as $X_{4(i-1)}$ at the joint $i > 1$. Then, if there are no cross members and the rate of twist flexibility at the ith joint is δ_{LQiF}, the nodal flexibility matrix becomes

$$\mathbf{D_F} = \begin{bmatrix} \delta_{LQ1F} & & & & & & & & \\ & 0 & & & & & & & \\ & & 0 & & & & & & \\ & & & \delta_{LQ2F} & & & & & \\ & & & & 0 & & & & \\ & & & & & 0 & & & \\ & & & & & & 0 & & \\ & & & & & & & \delta_{LQiF} & \\ & & & & & & & & \ddots \\ & & & & & & & & & \delta_{LQmF} \end{bmatrix} \qquad (12.54)$$

The analysis of commercial vehicle chassis frames   143

In the frame analysis so far the joints have been assumed to be point nodes. When the joints have extensive bracketry or gusset plates the analysis should be carried out by the method involving nodal substructures set out in chapter 9. The basic system used for this type of analysis is given in Fig. 12.19. The flexibility matrix for the cross member now becomes

$$
\mathbf{F}_{\mathrm{Qh}} =
\begin{bmatrix}
\dfrac{l_Q/2}{3\psi} & & \\
& \dfrac{l_Q/2}{\eta} & \dfrac{1}{\eta} \\
& \dfrac{1}{\eta} & \dfrac{\alpha}{\eta}\coth\alpha\,\dfrac{l_Q}{2}
\end{bmatrix}
\tag{12.55}
$$

where the subscripts 'h' are omitted from l_{Qh}, α_{h}, ψ_{h}, and η_{h}. The lengths of the side member beam elements, l_{L}, and the cross member element, l_{Q}, extend as far as the boundaries of the nodal areas, where l_{L} has to be used in the side member flexibility matrix, equation (12.36).

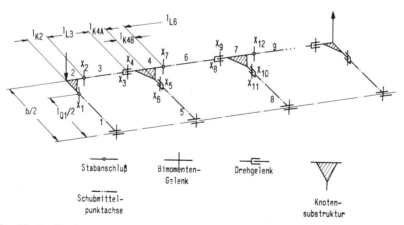

Stabanschluß   Bimomenten-   Drehgelenk
                      Gelenk

Schubmittel-   Knoten-
punktachse   substruktur

Fig. 12.19 **Statically determinate basic system for a frame with nodal substructures.**
Stabanschluß = beam element to joint connection
Bimomenten-Gelenk = bimoment hinge
Drehgekenk = torsion hinge
Knoten-substruktur = joint or nodal substructure
Schubmittelpunktachse = torsion centre axes

For torsional analysis, the joint substructure displacements required at the boundary are less than the complete set given in equation (9.1), and can be listed as

$$\beta_{y1s}, \beta_{x2s}, \beta_{y3s}, \varphi_{1s}, \varphi_{2s}, \varphi_{3s}, \varphi'_{1s}, \varphi'_{2s}, \text{ and } \varphi'_{3s}$$

The internal loads at the boundaries are similarly a part of the column vector in equation (9.2), see Fig. 9.3(b)

$$M_{y1s}, M_{x2s}, M_{y3s}, M_{D1s}, M_{D2s}, M_{D3s}, B_{1s}, B_{2s}, \text{ and } B_{3s}$$

The flexibility matrices $\mathbf{F}_{sh}$ to be found from the finite element analysis will therefore be 9×9 matrices.

It is impossible to use the symmetrical statically determinate support system of Fig. 9.3(a) for the joints at the ends of the front and rear cross members. It can be shown that it is sufficiently accurate to ignore the vertical bending deformation of the nodal substructure and the support system illustrated in Fig. 12.20 can be used for these joints. This only allows torques and bimoments to be applied to the joint substructure as shown, and the flexibility matrix is reduced to a 6×6, with zeros in the rows and columns corresponding to the vertical bending terms. The flexibility matrix, $\mathbf{F}_v$, can then be written, using the sequence indicated in Fig. 12.19, as

$$\mathbf{F}_v = \begin{bmatrix} \mathbf{F}_{Q1} & & & & & & \\ & \mathbf{F}_{s2} & & & & & \\ & & \mathbf{F}_{L3} & & & & \\ & & & \mathbf{F}_{s4} & & & \\ & & & & \mathbf{F}_{Q5} & & \\ & & & & & \mathbf{F}_{L6} & \\ & & & & & & \ddots \\ & & & & & & & \ddots \end{bmatrix} \qquad (12.56)$$

The values of the internal loads and displacements can be found from the method given in chapter 4, section 4.2, by using the $\mathbf{B}_0$, $\mathbf{B}_1$, and $\mathbf{F}_v$ matrices. By loading the substructures at the boundaries by the forces found from the analysis of the whole structure, the stresses in the nodal area can be found by finite element analysis, as in chapter 9.

When closed-section cross members are involved it is essential to include the torsional stiffness of the joint in the analysis, because the members themselves are substantially stiffer than open sections. This,

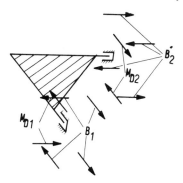

Fig. 12.20   Loads and supports at the boundaries of a nodal substructure at the ends of a frame, due to torsion

and the flexibility of the joint in bending about horizontal axes, will also be found from the substructure analysis suggested here. It can be shown that the flexibility of the nodal area corresponding to the profile deformation of the beam elements has little influence on the torsional stiffness of a frame with rectangular-section cross members, so this effect can be safely ignored in the case of closed-section cross members.

12.2.3   Effect of joint flexibility on horizontal bending

The deformation of the frame in horizontal bending is less important than the stresses generated by this type of loading. These stresses can only be found by using nodal substructures. The simpler point node approximation should be used when the lateral flexibility of the frame is required for the determination of the combined effect with other structures mounted on the frame. Only the analysis using substructures for finding the stress distribution will be given here.

The distribution of the bending moments shown in Fig. 12.8 depends on the flexural properties of the beam elements, e.g., a large bending moment will occur in a stiff cross member which will cause a big change in the bending moment in the side member on each side of it. The flexibility of the joints has an effect on this distribution and can therefore have a significant influence on the internal load distribution in the frame. For instance, even the rather stiff joint in Fig. 9.3 showed some flexibility when analysed by the finite element method. The slope β_{z2} at boundary 2 due to the bending moment M_{z2} was found to be 1.7 times greater than when the joint substructure shown was replaced by rigidly-jointed beam

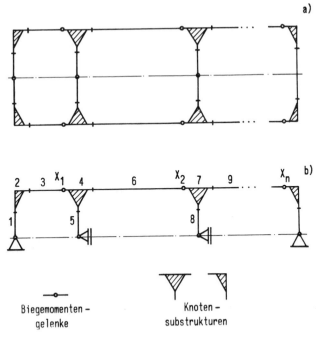

Fig. 12.21　(a)　**Statically determinate basic system for a frame with nodal substructures in horizontal bending**
　　　　　(b)　**Half the frame used for the analysis**
　　　　　[Biegemomentengelenke = bending moment hinge; Knotensubstrukturen = nodal substructures.]

elements of the same size. Nodal substructures are inserted into the frame shown in Fig. 12.7 to give the layout illustrated in Fig. 12.21(a). Because of symmetry only half the frame need be analysed, as indicated in Fig. 12.21(b). As in the case of vertical bending, the external load points at the ends of the frame can be taken as fictitious supports.

The beam elements have the displacement column vector

$$\mathbf{v}_h = \{u_h \quad \beta_{z1h} \quad \beta_{z2h}\}$$

and the internal loads at the ends

$$\mathbf{p}_h = \{N_h \quad M_{z1h} \quad M_{z2h}\}$$

The associated flexibility matrix for the side member beam elements comes from equation (4.16a) and reduces to

$$\mathbf{F}_{Lh} = \frac{I_h}{E} \begin{bmatrix} \dfrac{1}{A_h} & & \\ & \dfrac{1}{3J_{zh}} & -\dfrac{1}{6J_{zh}} \\ & -\dfrac{1}{6J_{zh}} & \dfrac{1}{3J_{zh}} \end{bmatrix} \qquad (12.57)$$

The flexibility matrix for half the cross member $\mathbf{F}_{Qh}$ is simple because $M_{z1h} = 0$ and the second row and column are omitted.

The displacements at the boundary of the nodal substructure, s, for horizontal bending can be listed as

$$u_{1s}, \ u_{2s}, \ u_{3s}, \ \beta_{z1s}, \ \beta_{z2s}, \ \text{and} \ \beta_{z3s}$$

and the loads on the same nodal substructure can be seen from Fig. 9.3(a) to be

$$N_{1s}, \ N_{2s}, \ N_{3s}, \ M_{z1s}, \ M_{z2s}, \ \text{and} \ M_{z3s}$$

Consequently the flexibility matrix, $\mathbf{F}_{sh}$, that has to be calculated by finite element methods for these nodal areas, is a 6×6 matrix.

The nodal substructures at the front and rear cross members and their statically determinate supports are shown in Fig. 12.22. Only the bending moments and one direct load are used as independent loads for the beam elements. The second direct load and the lateral loads, which are the

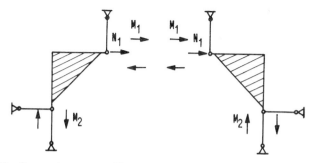

Fig. 12.22 Support system and internal loads for the substructures at the ends of the front and rear cross members due to horizontal bending

148   *The analysis of commercial vehicle structures*

support loads, can be found by using equilibrium conditions. The $\mathbf{B}_0$ and $\mathbf{B}_1$ matrices again contain the internal loads at the ends of the beam elements and the loads at the boundaries of the substructures for unit external loads and unit values of the redundant forces in Fig. 12.21, respectively. The internal loads and displacements can be found from the method given in chapter 4, section 4.2. Using the loads found at the boundaries of the substructures, the stress distribution in the nodal areas can then be found by the finite element method of chapter 9. The flexibility matrix, $\mathbf{F}_v$, is assembled with the sequence of beam and joint flexibilities indicated in Fig. 12.21 as

$$
\mathbf{F}_v = \begin{bmatrix} \mathbf{F}_{Q1} & & & & & \\ & \mathbf{F}_{s2} & & & & \\ & & \mathbf{F}_{L3} & & & \\ & & & \mathbf{F}_{s4} & & \\ & & & & \cdot & \\ & & & & & \cdot \\ & & & & & & \cdot \end{bmatrix} \tag{12.58}
$$

12.3 COUPLED TORSION AND HORIZONTAL BENDING

It has been assumed so far that the torsion or shear centre axes of the side members and cross members lie in the same plane. If the cross members are channel sections with horizontal webs it is clear that this assumption will not hold, and that in torsion the ends of the cross members will be displaced longitudinally if not restrained. Thus, the cross members will be bent about a vertical axis. Horizontal bending and torsion can no longer be treated independently and their stresses and displacements summed as before. This means that, to use the matrix force method, the structural systems shown diagrammatically in Figs 12.7 and 12.16, or 12.21 and 12.19, have to be combined into one system. The combined system is illustrated in Fig. 12.23, where the numbering for both the point node and the nodal substructure assumptions are shown. The notation for the redundant systems at the joints is, however, omitted. The unknown loads at the boundaries of the substructures were shown in Fig. 9.2, while Table 12.3 gives the positions of the redundant X loads and the zero loads in the basic system. When a redundant force occurs where three elements join, the internal load at the end of only one of the beams is zero in the basic system. This can be shown by considering the zero torque at end 2

Table 12.3   Positions of the zero loads due to the redundant loads in the basic system of Fig. 12.23

Point nodes			Nodal substructures		
Between beam numbers	*Redundant loads involved*	*Zero internal loads in basic system*	*Between beam numbers*	*Redundant loads involved*	*Zero internal loads in basic system*
1–2	X_1	$B_{21} = B_{12} = 0$	1–2	X_1	$B_{21} = B_{22} = 0$
			2–3	X_2	$B_{12} = B_{13} = 0$
2–3,4	X_2	$M_{D2} = 0$			
3–2,4	X_3	$M_{D3} = 0$	3–4	X_3	$M_{D3} = M_{D14} = 0$
3–2,4	X_4	$M_{z23} = 0$	3–4	X_4	$B_{23} = B_{14}$
2–3	X_5	$B_{22} = B_{23} = 0$			
2–4	X_6	$B_{14} = 0$	4–5	X_5	$M_{D24} = M_{D5} = 0$
			4–5	X_6	$M_{z24} = M_{z25} = 0$
4–5,6	X_7	$M_{D4} = 0$	4–5	X_7	$B_{24} = B_{25} = 0$
5–4,6	X_8	$M_{D5} = 0$			
5–4,6	X_9	$M_{z25} = 0$	4–6	X_8	$B_{34} = B_{16} = 0$
4–5	X_{10}	$B_{24} = B_{25} = 0$			
4–6	X_{11}	$B_{16} = 0$	⋮		
X_{11} is omitted if mode 3 is at the end of the frame			a–b	X_e	$M_{Da} = M_{D1b} = 0$
			a–b	X_f	$B_{2a} = B_{1b} = 0$
			b–c	X_g	$M_{D2b} = M_{Dc} = 0$
			b–c	X_h	$M_{z2b} = M_{z2c} = 0$
			b–c	X_j	$B_{2b} = B_{2c} = 0$
			b–d	X_k	$B_{3b} = B_{1d} = 0$
			X_k is omitted if mode i is at the end of a frame		

of beam 2, Fig. 12.23(a) or Fig. 12.16, where the bending moment in beam 3, M_{x23}, and the torque in beam 4, M_{D4}, are equal because of equilibrium at the joint. The redundant loads are numbered consecutively at each joint in Fig. 12.23(a) to improve clarity. The redundancies at joint i can be summarized as $X_{5(i-1)-3}$ to $X_{5(i-1)+1}$. The number of columns in the matrix $\mathbf{B}_1$ is the number of the redundancies, and the rows contain all the internal loads at the ends of the beam elements, as indicated in Table 12.2.

The effect of staggering the torsion centres of either one or two of the cross members of a four-cross-member frame is shown in Fig. 12.24. These results were found by calculation, assuming they were stiff in bending, and are taken from reference (**11**). [Although the figure shows

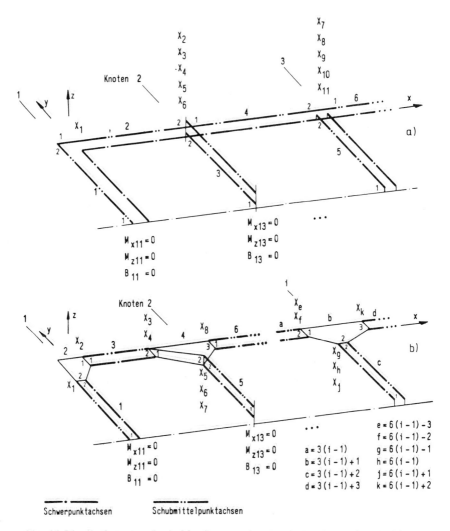

Fig. 12.23   **Basic system for ladder frames when torsion centre and centroid axes do not coincide:**
(a) **using point nodes**
(b) **using nodal substructures**
   Schwerpunktachsen = centroid axes
   Schubmittellpunktachsen = torsion centre axes

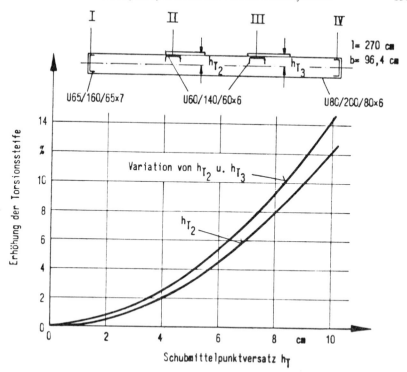

Fig. 12.24 **Example of the effect of staggering vertically the torsion centres of cross members on the torsional stiffness of a ladder frame.**
Erhöhung der Torsionssteife = increase in torsional stiffness
Schubmittelpunktversatz = difference in height of the torsion centres

h_T just more than the height of the web of the two cross members above the centre line of the frame, this difference should be greater since the axis of the graph is the height of the torsion centre above the centreline.]

Although the torsional stiffness of the frame is increased because of the horizontal bending of the two cross members caused by twisting about their torsion centres when they are staggered, the absolute torsional stiffness is largely dependent on the two full-depth channel-section cross members with vertical webs at the ends of the frame.

The frameworks discussed so far have been made of constant-section, thin-walled, straight, beam elements. In some designs the profile of the

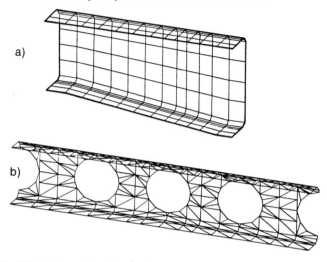

Fig. 12.25   Finite element meshes for:
(a)   side member section with tapered depth of web
(b)   cross member with lightening holes

beam elements may change along their length, or one or more of the cross members, and even the side members, may be bent normal to the plane of the frame. The bends usually coincide with a change in the profile of the cross section. The flexibility matrices in these cases have to be found by finite element analysis in the same way as for the nodal substructures. That is, by introducing unit internal loads at the ends of the beams and condensing the displacements of the nodes in the finite element idealization to define the required displacement components of the end cross section of the beam element. Figure 12.25 shows two examples of members with variable cross sections. Figure 12.25(a) is a tapered side member with linearly variable height, and Fig. 12.25(b) a side member with large lightening holes in the web. It can be shown that the torsional flexibility, the twist per unit torque, and the rate of twist per unit bimoment increase roughly linearly with the area of the holes in the web for channel-section cross members, see reference (**11**). It can also be shown that lightening holes in the web reduce the weight more than they reduce the torsional stiffness, in percentage terms, without greatly increasing the stresses.

Tapering the side member by raising the lower flange while leaving the

a)

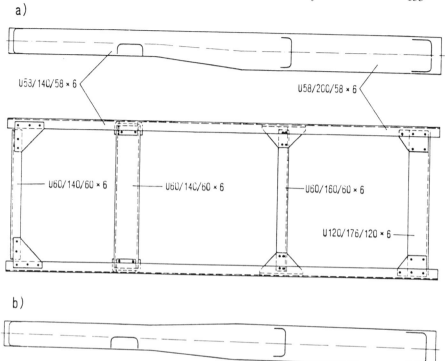

U53/140/58 × 6

U58/200/58 × 6

U60/140/60 × 6   U60/140/60 × 6   U60/160/60 × 6

U120/176/120 × 6

b)

Fig. 12.26   Three bay frame with tapered side members:
(a)   unsymmetrical taper, lower flange raised
(b)   symmetrical taper

upper flange horizontal means that the centroid axis is no longer in the
plane of the frame. This causes a coupling between the horizontal bending
and torsion of the frame. However, reference (9) shows that the effect on
the torsional stiffness and stress distribution is only significant if the
centroid axis is displaced by a distance of the same order as the height of
the web in the parallel section of the side member. If the taper only results
in the centroid axis moving a few centimetres it is recommended that the
coupling is neglected in the frame analysis and that basic systems of the
type shown in Figs 12.16 and 12.23 be used. For an accurate analysis it is
necessary to use a finite element method to find the flexibility matrix in the
area of the side member where it is tapering and where the cross section
is reduced. The 3-bay symmetrically-tapered frame shown in Fig. 12.26(b)

was found to have only 4 per cent greater torsional stiffness than the unsymmetrically tapered one shown in Fig. 12.26(a). This difference is negligible when the difference in the dimensions of the commercial sections used, the variation of welded joints, etc., are taken into account. Frames may also be tapered in the horizontal plane to change the width; for instance, the width may be reduced in the rear axle area. Such tapers cause a change in the basic systems used so far, and the $\mathbf{B}_0$ and $\mathbf{B}_1$ matrices become slightly more elaborate. Frames of this type have been analysed by the matrix force method and the results have been verified by test. The torsional stiffness is again increased when the width is reduced, because the shorter cross members have greater torsional stiffness due to the effect of warping inhibition, which is particularly marked if the joints are stiff in respect of rate of twist. The stresses are also greater in the narrow part of the frame than in the wide part, for the same reason.

When cross members are bent vertically to accommodate transmission or running units the flexibility matrices have to be found by finite element methods. In many designs the joint nodal substructures can be extended to include the length of the cross member where the bending takes place and the centre part of the cross member treated as a straight beam with a vertically staggered centroid axis, as shown above, so that these cross members again have a coupling between torsion and horizontal bending.

12.4 APPROXIMATE TORSIONAL DYNAMIC ANALYSIS

The stiffness matrix in the dynamic equation (1.3) can be found for chassis frames which carry non-self-supporting structures, by using the static stiffness analysis given above to find the load–deflection characteristics of the frame. For the mass matrix it is normally sufficient to use a lumped mass idealization with the masses concentrated at the joints of the frame. If necessary, additional lumped masses can be placed within the length of the cross members or the sections of side members between the cross-member joints.

In order to use conventional computer programs for the dynamic analysis of torsion it is necessary to specify simple beam elements of the type contained in the program, rather than the elaborate beam elements and flexible nodes or nodal substructures discussed above. However, the cross-sectional data of the beam elements input to the program must have the same load–deflection behaviour as those calculated by the methods of this chapter which have been verified by tests. The beam elements in most programs do not include the effect of warping inhibition and, therefore, the St Venant torsion constant, J_t, to be used in the program must be replaced by an effective torsion constant, J_t^{**}, defined by

$$J_{th}^{**} = \frac{M_{Dh}}{G\vartheta} \tag{12.59}$$

where M_{Dh} is the torque acting on beam h, which could be either a cross member or a section of a side member. As shown in section 12.1, the rate of twist is the same in all the beams when bending is ignored. This assumption is valid for torsionally flexible commercial vehicle chassis frames. The effective torsion constant, J_{th}^{*}, defined in chapter 12.1 assumed that the rate of twist was zero at the ends of the beam elements since the joints were taken as rigid. Here, however, the torque M_{Dh} and the average rate of twist are found from the frame analysis given in section 12.2, which includes the effect of warping and flexible joints. In this way the dynamic analysis itself remains simple while the elaborate static frame analysis of section 12.2 is effectively utilized. It is, of course, necessary to check back that the element cross-sectional data used does give the same frame deflection as the elaborate analysis.

The friction generated by slipping in the joints of a frame, described in chapter 11, can have an important effect on the dynamic torsional behaviour of the frame. The movement in the joint causes frictional damping and also reduces the torsional stiffness. The hysteresis and change of slope with amplitude illustrated in Fig. 11.3 demonstrates both of these effects. If these effects are not taken into account in the analysis the result will only be correct for small oscillations. There are no general rules for calculating the frequencies of a frame where the stiffness reduces with increasing amplitude. Since there is not sufficient knowledge of the static properties, this places a limitation on the dynamic analysis of real frames. The friction between a superstructure and the frame can have a substantially greater effect on the vibration of a complete vehicle than the friction in the chassis frame.

13

Bus frameworks

The superstructures of buses are so stiff that, even if they are mounted on chassis frames which have been designed to carry all the required load, the load will be shared with the body structure. Some buses have integral steel framework structures which carry all the running loads; other successful designs of city buses have underfloor steel tubular framework structures which share the load with the superstructure. Figure 13.1 illustrates the fundamental structure of such a design. The underfloor structures of touring coaches are normally designed with no diagonal members in the centre longitudinal bays so that baggage can be handled from the sides of the bus and carried in full width luggage bays. The underfloor framework, which can absorb both bending and torsion, is connected by underfloor cross members to the side walls of the superstructure. Alternatively a design could be made with longitudinals and cross members extended to the side walls in place of the centre underfloor framework, which would have the advantages of considerably fewer

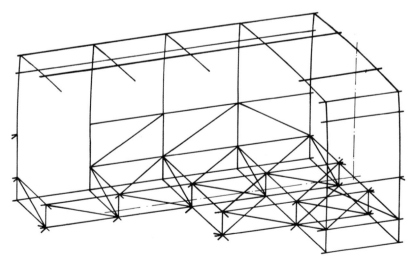

Fig. 13.1   Section of a typical integral bus framework

welded joints and lower height, but which would contain more material and consequently be heavier.

Tubular frameworks can easily be analysed by standard computer programs. As opposed to the case with chassis frames, the dimensions of the nodal areas at the joints are small compared with the lengths of the members, so that the joint flexibilities have less effect. It is well known that a good approximation to the load distribution in frameworks can even be obtained with the assumption of pin joints. As an example, a bus side frame analysed as a pin-jointed framework gave an error of only 1–2 per cent in the direct loads in the members, compared with a stiff-jointed analysis. However, because the joints are actually stiff, bending stresses occur in the members, which can lead to a considerable increase in the total stresses over those due to the direct loads. The stresses in the joints can be obtained from a finite element analysis.

The framework of the side walls is reinforced by the sheet metal cladding and glazing. The shear load would be shared between the framework and cladding if it were attached to all the tubular members and if it were sufficiently pretensioned. Normally, however, these assumptions are not sufficiently fulfilled to base an accurate analysis on them. The cladding of the roof, is, however, very important when the vehicle is in torsion. The half-scale model shown in Fig. 13.2 gave a measured increase in torsional stiffness of 60 per cent when the roof was covered with sheet metal which was not pretensioned and which was attached by adhesive. The effect of glazing on the structure is discussed in section 13.3.

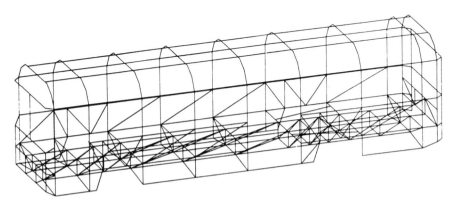

Fig. 13.2   Simplified half scale model of a bus framework structure

13.1 INTERACTION OF UNDERFLOOR STRUCTURE AND SUPERSTRUCTURE

It is easier to understand the behaviour of large structures if they are divided into substructures and the interactions between them can be fully understood. The term 'bus superstructure' here means the separate substructures of the side walls, the roof, and the front and rear frames. The underfloor structure is defined as the box-girder framework at the centre of the floor. The superstructure is fixed to the ends of the cross members which run across the underfloor structure, and may form part of it, but whose outrigger parts provide a flexible element in the connection between the two main substructures.

Vertical bending
Both the superstructure and the underfloor structure are loaded by external vertical forces and the internal forces at the connections between the two structures, which are usually at the outer ends of the cross members for the superstructure and at the inner ends of the outrigger sections of the cross members for the underfloor structure. The elastic interaction of the various substructures is the most important factor in this analysis, and the formulae required are given in this section.

Influence coefficients are used to define the displacements of nodal points relative to reference points. The reference points used are the intersections of the columns of the side walls with the cross members at the numbered cross sections in Fig. 13.3(a), as well as the points 2 and 8 in Fig. 13.3(b). These two points are the front engine mount of the rear engine and the centre line of the front axle mountings. The vertical displacement of the lower flange of the side wall and the upper flange of the underfloor structure are obtained by assuming that the reference points at the front and rear ends; points 1 and 10 in Fig. 13.3, are fictitious fixed supports, as in chapter 12, section 12.1.

The influence coefficients for the side walls and roof considered as a substructure are defined as follows. The influence coefficient a_{ij} is the displacement of the lower longitudinal of the side wall at cross section i due to a unit load acting at the lower longitudinal or lower flange of the side wall at cross section j. The influence coefficient linking the same sections of the underfloor structure is b_{ij}, where the points are taken at the upper flanges of the vertical sides of this substructure in the relevant cross section. This definition of the influence coefficients means that the a_{ij}

terms include the effect of the different stiffnesses of the two side frames, one having door openings, as in the structure of Fig. 13.3. There will be a small internal torsion induced in the superstructure from this asymmetry, but it can be ignored in this treatment.

The influence coefficients can be arranged in flexibility matrices as follows

$$\mathbf{F}_{aa} = \begin{bmatrix} 0 & 0 & 0 & \cdots & 0 & 0 \\ 0 & a_{2\,2} & a_{2\,3} & \cdots & a_{2\,n-1} & 0 \\ 0 & a_{3\,2} & a_{3\,3} & \cdots & a_{3\,n-1} & 0 \\ \vdots & \vdots & \vdots & & \vdots & \vdots \\ 0 & a_{n-1\,2} & \cdots & & a_{n-1\,n-1} & 0 \\ 0 & 0 & \cdots & & 0 & 0 \end{bmatrix} \quad (13.1)$$

and

$$\mathbf{F}_{bb} = \begin{bmatrix} 0 & 0 & 0 & \cdots & 0 & 0 \\ 0 & b_{2\,2} & b_{2\,3} & \cdots & b_{2\,n-1} & 0 \\ 0 & b_{3\,2} & b_{3\,3} & \cdots & b_{3\,n-1} & 0 \\ \vdots & \vdots & \vdots & & \vdots & \vdots \\ 0 & b_{n-1\,2} & \cdots & & b_{n-1\,n-1} & 0 \\ 0 & 0 & \cdots & & 0 & 0 \end{bmatrix} \quad (13.2)$$

Since the fictitious supports of both these systems are at the front and rear ends of the structures, the top and bottom rows and the first and last columns will only contain zeros. If there are q external loads acting on the superstructure the corresponding flexibility matrix will be

$$\mathbf{F}_{ad} = \begin{bmatrix} 0 & 0 & \cdots & 0 \\ d_{2\,1} & d_{2\,2} & \cdots & d_{2\,q} \\ \vdots & \vdots & & \vdots \\ d_{n-1\,1} & d_{n-1\,2} & \cdots & d_{n-1\,q} \\ 0 & 0 & \cdots & 0 \end{bmatrix} \quad (13.3)$$

where the influence coefficients are d_{ij} for the displacements at the lower

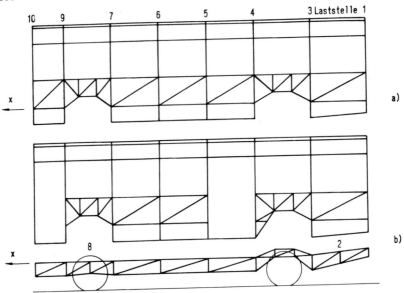

Fig. 13.3 **Loading points (reference points) in the vertical plane:**
     (a)   **for the superstructure, i.e., side walls and roof**
     (b)   **for the underfloor structure**
     [Laststelle = loading point.]

flanges of the side walls. Similarly the flexibility matrix for the underfloor
structure corresponding to r external loads will be

$$\mathbf{F}_{be} = \begin{bmatrix} 0 & 0 & \cdots & 0 \\ e_{2\,1} & e_{2\,2} & \cdots & e_{2\,r} \\ \vdots & \vdots & & \vdots \\ e_{n-1\,1} & e_{n-1\,2} & \cdots & e_{n-1\,r} \\ 0 & 0 & \cdots & 0 \end{bmatrix} \qquad (13.4)$$

So long as the load points or reference points of both the internal and
the external loads are the same – in this case they coincide with the
columns of the side walls – a_{ij} and d_{ij} are identical, as are b_{ij} and e_{ij} for the
underfloor structure. The example structure shown in Figure 13.3 has
load points 2 and 8 which are on cross sections which do not coincide with
underfloor cross members, so that the matrices $\mathbf{F}_{aa}$, $\mathbf{F}_{bb}$, and $\mathbf{F}_{ad}$ will have

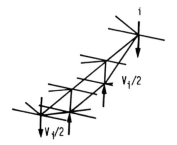

Fig. 13.4   Vertical loads transferred by a cross member

the 2nd and 8th rows and columns all zero, as well as the 2nd and 8th rows in $\mathbf{F}_{be}$. The total vertical displacements of the superstructure at the load points are

$$\mathbf{w}_a = \{w_{a1} \ \ldots \ w_{ai} \ \ldots \ w_{an}\} \qquad (13.5)$$

and those of the underfloor structure

$$\mathbf{w}_b = \{w_{b1} \ \ldots \ w_{bi} \ \ldots \ w_{bn}\} \qquad (13.6)$$

The flexibility of the outrigger portions of the cross members cause vertical displacements of the side wall joints relative to the upper flange of the underfloor structure which can be expressed as the column matrix

$$\mathbf{w}_c = \{f_1 \ \ldots \ f_i \ \ldots \ f_n\} \qquad (13.7)$$

where a positive value of f corresponds to a downward displacement of the side wall joint. The force V_1 causing this displacement at the ith cross member is illustrated in Fig. 13.4 and is defined so that a positive value supports the superstructure and loads the underfloor structure. As in the illustration, the loads on the cross member are arranged so that the loads on the structures are equal and opposite

$$V_i = -V_{ai} = V_{bi} \qquad (13.8)$$

If the stiffness of the outrigger portion of the cross member is c_i at the ith cross section, the corresponding displacement to V_i will be

$$f_i = \frac{1}{c_i} V_i \qquad (13.9)$$

so that a flexibility matrix for these parts of the cross members can be written

$$\mathbf{F}_c = \begin{bmatrix} 1/c_1 & & & & & \\ & \cdot & & & & \\ & & \cdot & & & \\ & & & \cdot & & \\ & & & 1/c_i & & \\ & & & & \cdot & \\ & & & & & \cdot \\ & & & & & & \cdot \\ & & & & & & & 1/c_n \end{bmatrix} \qquad (13.10)$$

The external loads acting on the superstructure can be arranged in the column matrix

$$\mathbf{f}_a = \{F_{a1} \ \ldots \ F_{ak} \ \ldots \ F_{aq}\} \qquad (13.11)$$

and the external loads acting on the underfloor structure can be similarly arranged as

$$\mathbf{f}_b = \{F_{b1} \ \ldots \ F_{bl} \ \ldots \ F_{br}\} \qquad (13.12)$$

the forces in the cross members given in equation (13.8) can also be arranged in a column matrix

$$\mathbf{f}_c = \{V_1 \ \ldots \ V_i \ V_n\} \qquad (13.13)$$

The vertical displacements of the superstructure now become

$$\mathbf{w}_a = -\mathbf{F}_{aa}\mathbf{f}_c + \mathbf{F}_{ad}\mathbf{f}_a \qquad (13.14)$$

and the displacements of the underfloor framework are

$$\mathbf{w}_b = \mathbf{F}_{bb}\mathbf{f}_c + \mathbf{F}_{be}\mathbf{f}_b \qquad (13.15)$$

finally the displacements of the outrigger portions of the cross members are

$$\mathbf{w}_c = \mathbf{F}_c\mathbf{f}_c \qquad (13.16)$$

For compatibility of the displacements of the superstructure and the underfloor structure the relative displacements of the two structures, f_1 and f_n, at cross sections 1 and n must be taken into account. From simple geometry this leads to a relative rigid body displacement at the ith cross section of

$$f_{Ri} = f_1 + (f_n - f_1)\frac{x_i}{x_n} \tag{13.17}$$

leading to a column matrix of displacements

$$\mathbf{w}_R = \{f_{R1} \cdots f_{Ri} \cdots f_{Rn}\} \tag{13.18}$$

Which, in turn, can be written as a product of a flexibility matrix and the cross member forces taken from equation (13.13), so that

$$\mathbf{w}_R = \mathbf{F}_R\mathbf{f}_c \tag{13.19}$$

The flexibility matrix itself is obtained from the individual terms given by equation (13.17) with the displacements substituted from equation (13.9). Since cross section 1 is at $x = 0$, $x_1 = 0$, flexibility matrix is now

$$\mathbf{F}_R = \begin{bmatrix} \dfrac{1}{c_1} & & 0 & \cdots & 0 & 0 \\[2ex] \left(1 - \dfrac{x_2}{x_n}\right)\dfrac{1}{c_1} & & 0 & \cdots & 0 & \dfrac{x_2}{x_n}\dfrac{1}{c_n} \\[2ex] \vdots & & & & & \vdots \\[2ex] \left(1 - \dfrac{x_{n-1}}{x_n}\right)\dfrac{1}{c_1} & & 0 & \cdots & 0 & \dfrac{x_{n-1}}{x_n}\dfrac{1}{c_n} \\[2ex] 0 & & 0 & \cdots & 0 & \dfrac{1}{c_n} \end{bmatrix} \tag{13.20}$$

The total displacement of the superstructure relative to the undisplaced underfloor structure is $\mathbf{w}_a + \mathbf{w}_R$, so that the compatibility equation for the points along the structure is

$$\mathbf{w}_a + \mathbf{w}_R - \mathbf{w}_b = \mathbf{w}_c \tag{13.21}$$

substituting equations (13.14, 15, 16, and 19) in (13.21) gives

$$(-\mathbf{F}_{aa} - \mathbf{F}_{bb} + \mathbf{F}_R - \mathbf{F}_c)\mathbf{f}_c + \mathbf{F}_{ad}\mathbf{f}_a - \mathbf{F}_{be}\mathbf{f}_b = \mathbf{o} \tag{13.22}$$

The first and last equations in the set (13.22) are eliminated because the corresponding rows are all zeros in the flexibility matrices $\mathbf{F}_{aa}$, $\mathbf{F}_{ad}$, $\mathbf{F}_{bb}$, $\mathbf{F}_{be}$, and equal in the matrices $\mathbf{F}_R$ and $\mathbf{F}_c$. Two further conditions required for the solution are that the mutual forces between the substructures and

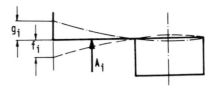

Fig. 13.5 Deformation of the outrigger section of a cross member due to a suspension load, A_i

the external forces acting on the superstructure must be in equilibrium. This applies, of course, to both the direct forces and moments.

The suspension system may load an outrigger portion of a cross member somewhere between the underfloor structure and the side wall. This is especially true for air suspensions which are now almost universal. These additional load points can be incorporated into the calculation by adding the displacement, g_i, at the side wall, due to the suspension load, A_i, to the displacement of the outrigger part, f_i, as shown in Fig. 13.5. So that

$$g_i = \frac{1}{c_{Ai}} A_i \qquad (13.23)$$

the corresponding flexibility matrix is

$$\mathbf{F}_{cA} = \begin{bmatrix} 0 & & & & \\ & \cdot & & & \\ & & \cdot & & \\ & & & \cdot & \\ & & 1/c_{Ai} & & \\ & & & \cdot & \\ & & & & \cdot \end{bmatrix} \qquad (13.24)$$

while the suspension forces can be arranged as

$$\mathbf{f}_A = \{0 \ \ldots \ A_i \ \ldots\} \qquad (13.25)$$

Besides the vertical loads on the vehicle there can also be horizontal loads and moments about horizontal axes, as defined in load case II, chapter 3. These loads acting at cross section m can be arranged as the column matrices

$$\mathbf{f}_{bL} = \{\ldots L_m \ldots\}; \quad \mathbf{f}_{bM} = \{\ldots M_m \ldots\} \qquad (13.26)$$

with the corresponding influence coefficients arranged in the flexibility matrices

$$\mathbf{F}_{bL} = [l_{im}]; \qquad \mathbf{F}_{bm} = [m_{im}] \qquad (13.27)$$

The compatibility equation (13.22) can now be extended to include the effect of the suspension mountings by adding the terms in equations (13.24, 25, 26, and 27) to give

$$(-\mathbf{F}_{aa} - \mathbf{F}_{bb} + \mathbf{F}_R - \mathbf{F}_c)\mathbf{f}_c + \mathbf{F}_{ad}\mathbf{f}_a + \mathbf{F}_{be}\mathbf{f}_b + \mathbf{F}_{cA}\mathbf{f}_A - \mathbf{F}_{bm}\mathbf{f}_{bm}$$
$$- \mathbf{F}_{bL}\mathbf{f}_{bL} = \mathbf{0} \qquad (13.28)$$

These matrix relationships include the effect of the interaction of the two substructures which are elastically connected by the outrigger portions of the cross members.

As an example of the results of the vertical bending analysis, Fig. 13.6 shows the bending moment diagrams for the two substructures and half the total bending moment diagram for the bus structure of Fig. 13.3 under static loading. It has been assumed in the analysis that the rear suspension has two air suspension units at each side of the vehicle. One at cross section 3 behind the axle near the side wall, the other at cross section 4 in front of the axle and near the underfloor structure. The front suspension has only one air suspension unit on each side and this is at section 8 and acts directly on the underfloor structure. It is important to note that in this example the bending moment carried by the underfloor substructure over the front axle is much greater than the mean bending moment of the whole structure at this point, since only the underfloor structure is loaded by the front axle support load. Figure 13.7 shows the displacements of the superstructure and the underfloor structure when the base line has been moved from the line joining the underfloor structure at the front and rear of the vehicle to the line joining the underfloor structure at the front and rear axle positions.

To complete the estimation of the load-carrying properties of the bus structure in bending, it is necessary to carry out a similar stress and displacement analysis for load cases II and V chapter 3.

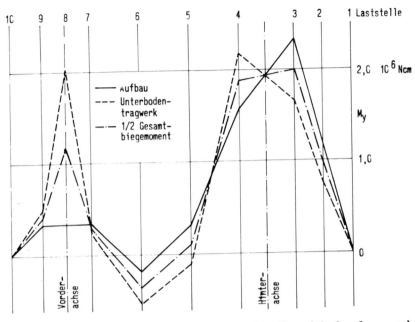

Fig. 13.6 **Bending moment diagram for vertical loading of the bus framework shown in Fig. 13.3.**
[Aufbau = superstructure; Unterboden-tragwerk = underfloor structure; $\frac{1}{2}$ Gesamt-biegemoment = half total bending moment; Vorderachse = front axle; Hinterachse = rear axle.]

Torsion

The superstructure and underfloor structure act as two parallel tubes in torsion, with the floor acting as the interface. This is illustrated in Fig. 13.8, where s_{AB} is the width of the floor, and the separate structures are A and B. Bredt's classical theory of tubes in parallel assumes that the shear flow in the interface is in the opposite direction for the two substructures. From the theory of parallel tubes with a common interface it follows that

$$\frac{M_{DA}}{M_{DB}} = \frac{c_{TA} + T}{c_{TB} + T} \tag{13.29}$$

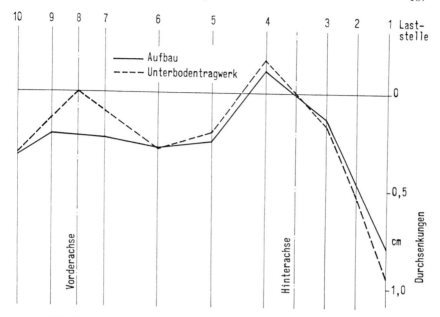

Fig. 13.7 Deformation of the superstructure and underfloor structure of the framework shown in Fig. 13.3 in bending.
[Durchsenkungen = downward displacement.]

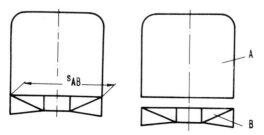

Fig. 13.8 Superstructure, A, and underfloor structure, B, with the floor as the interface

where c_{TA} and c_{TB} are the torsional stiffnesses of the superstructure and the underfloor structure, respectively. Simple expressions can be found for the sums in the numerator and denominator when the interface is a shear panel. The top face of the underfloor structure is not a shear panel, but the effect of the additional term, T, is to bring the torques acting on the two substructures closer together than would be the case if

$$\frac{M_{DA}}{M_{DB}} = \frac{c_{TA}}{c_{TB}}$$

There will be an increase in the overall torsional stiffness because the torsion axes of the two parallel structures do not coincide, as was the case for the chassis and superstructures of commercial vehicles in chapter 11. This means that the sum of the torques in the two substructures will be less than the total torque acting on the bus, i.e.

$$M_{DA} + M_{DB} < M_D$$

When a first estimate of the sizes of members is required the two torques can each be taken as 40 per cent of the total torque on the structure.

When research into the interaction of the substructures is to be carried out, or a more exact value of the distribution of the total torque is required it is necessary to use influence coefficients as for the bending analysis. The underfloor structure is now taken to include the whole of the cross members as well as the central box-girder tubular framework, but not the longitudinal members at floor height in the side walls, which are, of course, included in the side walls themselves. The coupling forces at the joints between the substructures now include both vertical and horizontal components, so that there will be influence coefficients in both directions. Mutual rigid body displacements between the substructures must be prevented and the points chosen to define the position of the two structures will, as in the bending case, be the same points as those used for the statically determinate support system which the influence coefficients are based on. The mutual loads at the other coupling points deform both of the substructures. These loads, which follow from the compatibility conditions at these points, and the equilibrium conditions for the rigid body loads are sufficient to solve the resulting matrix equations.

The influence coefficients for the superstructure refer to the displacements of the joints at the outer ends of the cross members for unit loads at the other cross sections and can be arranged in the flexibility matrix

$$\mathbf{F}_a = \begin{bmatrix} a_{1x1x} & a_{1x1z} & a_{1x2x} & a_{1x2z} & \cdots \\ a_{1z1x} & a_{1z1z} & a_{1z2x} & \cdots \\ a_{2x1x} & a_{2x1z} & \cdots \\ \vdots \\ a_{nz1x} & & & & a_{nznz} \end{bmatrix} \qquad (13.30)$$

As in the bending analysis, the superstructure includes the side walls and the roof. The flexibility matrix $\mathbf{F}_a$ differs from $\mathbf{F}_{aa}$ in equation (13.1) as it includes the horizontal components and the vertical components are not the same because the support system is different. The equivalent flexibility matrix for the underfloor structure will be $\mathbf{F}_B$, which contains influence coefficients of the side wall to cross member joints. The subscript 'B' is used to distinguish these influence coefficients from the influence coefficients of the central points used for the bending analysis, where the subscript 'b' was used. The displacements of the underfloor structure at the side wall to cross member joints due to the external torsion loads are expressed as influence coefficients which can be arranged in the flexibility matrix $\mathbf{F}_{BF}$ so that the compatibility equation becomes

$$(\mathbf{F}_a - \mathbf{F}_B)\mathbf{f}_v - \mathbf{F}_{BF}\mathbf{f}_b = \mathbf{o} \qquad (13.31)$$

where the column matrix of the coupling forces is

$$\mathbf{f}_v \{V_{1x} \ V_{1z} \ V_{2x} \ \ldots\} \qquad (13.32)$$

and the external torsional loads acting on the underfloor structure are in the column matrix $\mathbf{f}_b$.

The compatibility equations, (13.22) or (13.28), which were used to solve for the bending displacements of the two substructures only contained single influence coefficients. A similar solution can be found for the interaction of the two substructures if equation (13.31) is extended by a term giving the displacements of the superstructure due to the external loads. This will be obtained from the product of the flexibility matrix, $\mathbf{F}_{aF}$, which is the matrix of the displacements due to unit external loads acting on the superstructure and the column matrix of the external loads acting on the superstructure, $\mathbf{f}_a$. This compatibility equation now becomes

$$(\mathbf{F}_a - \mathbf{F}_B)\mathbf{f}_v + \mathbf{F}_{aF}\mathbf{f}_a - \mathbf{F}_{BF}\mathbf{f}_b = \mathbf{o} \qquad (13.33)$$

The rows and columns corresponding to the rigid body coupling terms are zeros in the F_a and F_B matrices. As in the bending case, there are sufficient equilibrium equations to solve the problem. Using equation (13.33), which gives the effect of the interaction between the two substructures, the static behaviour of the individual substructures can be analysed.

13.2 APPROXIMATE CALCULATIONS TO FIND INITIAL DIMENSIONS

The first step in design analysis is always to find approximate dimensions for the main structural members which can then be used as the initial values in a thorough analysis of the kind that has been suggested in the first part of this chapter. The dimensions of the members can then be changed to ensure that the total stresses are within the strength limits, or the fatigue limits, of the material to be used. These approximate calculations are usually based on experience and very simple methods of analysis. The aim is to find the normal loads, bending moments, and torques in the beam elements for the combinations of load cases listed in chapter 3 which may occur in practice. The way the loads are allocated to the substructures has to be estimated by the method defined in the first part of this chapter.

Vertical bending
The superstructure is analysed as a two-flanged beam consisting of the side wall up to the waist rail, ignoring the window pillars, roof, and cant rail. The underfloor structure can similarly be considered as a two flanged beam with the upper flange at floor level. The loads in the beam elements can be found directly by Ritter's method for pin-jointed frameworks. Figure 13.9 shows the ith bay of either of these beams, where the moments M_{yi} and M_{yi+1} are the bending moments in the bay at the load points i and $i + 1$. The shear force between these two points is defined as

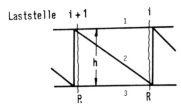

Fig. 13.9   Illustration of Ritter's method of sections in one bay of the two-flanged framework beam forming the side of an underfloor structure

$Q_{zi \div i+1}$. The direct loads in the members simply follow from equilibrium and are given by

$$N_1 = M_{yi}/h$$
$$N_3 = M_{yi+1}/h \qquad (13.34)$$
$$N_2 = Q_{zi \div i+1} l_2/h$$

It has been proved that a good approximation can be made to the problem of finding the bending moment in a door frame by the following assumption. If i and $i + 1$ are the load points at the door pillars and the bending moments on the side wall at these points are $\frac{1}{2}M_{yAi}$ and $\frac{1}{2}M_{yA+1}$, the change in the bending moment between the door columns is

$$\Delta(\tfrac{1}{2}M_{yA}) = \tfrac{1}{2}M_{yAi} - \tfrac{1}{2}M_{yAi+1}$$

This change in bending moment is split equally giving the bending moments at the corners of the door frame approximately equal to $\Delta(\tfrac{1}{2}M_{yA})/4$, as shown in Fig. 13.10. This assumes that the shear over the door opening is shared equally between the sill and the cantrail. The comparison with the exact calculation is shown to be very good in this example.

Torsion

When the superstructure is in torsion the window pillars are in bending due to opposing longitudinal forces in the cant rail and waist rail, or, in the case of the door pillars, the cant rail and sill member. Figure 13.11 shows the shear flow in the superstructure for this load case. Below the waist rail the shear is carried by the diagonal members in the framework. The shear flow caused by a torque M_{DA} is found from Bredt's first formula as

$$q_A = \frac{M_{DA}}{2A_A} \qquad (13.35)$$

where A_A is the cross sectional area of the superstructure regarded as a longitudinal tube. The shear flow, q_A, can be used to find the approximate bending moment in the window pillars. This shear flow, however, has proved to be unsuitable for finding the torsional stiffness of the superstructure as a tube. This is because the cross sections are not sufficiently stiff in their own plane. This can be seen from the calculated shear deformations of the cross sections of the bus superstructure in torsion, shown to an enlarged scale in Fig. 13.12. Figure 13.13 shows the deformation of the complete bus frame. For these calculations it was

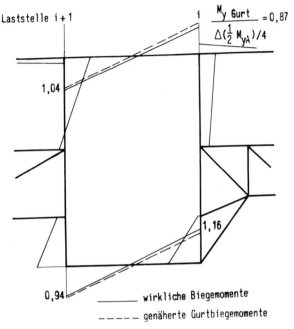

Fig. 13.10   **Comparison of the approximate and exact bending moment distributions round a door frame.**
**[Wirkliche Biegemomente = exact analysis; Genäherte Gurtbiege-
momente = approximate calculation.]**

assumed that the bus framework, which was that shown in Fig. 13.2, had
the metal cladding fitted.

The method to be used for the approximate analysis of the underfloor
structure can be illustrated by considering the mth bay of the hollow
box-girder framework shown in Fig. 13.14. This kind of three dimensional
framework can be simply analysed assuming pin-jointed members.
Longitudinal members ending in a joint where there is no diagonal
member in the side, top, or bottom plane cannot transfer a longitudinal
load, i.e., they are not load-carrying members. They are shown crossed in
Fig. 13.14. The remaining members in the side, top, and bottom planes
have to carry the torque M_D. The longitudinal components of load in each
pair of these members are in equilibrium, thus, since

$$l_a = \sqrt{(a^2 + l^2)}; \quad l_b = \sqrt{(b^2 + l^2)} \qquad (13.36)$$

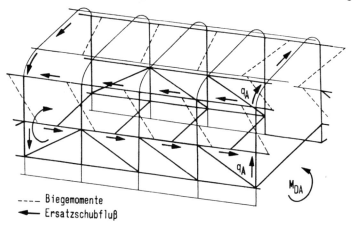

---- Biegemomente
◄— Ersatzschubfluβ

Fig. 13.11 **Shear flow direction in the superstructure under torsion and the bending moment distribution in the window and door pillars. [Biegemomente = bending moment; Ersatzschubfluβ = shear flow.]**

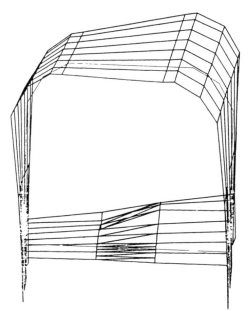

Fig. 13.12 **Calculated shear deformation of the cross sections of the superstructure of the bus shown in Fig. 13.2 in torsion. Displacements shown enlarged**

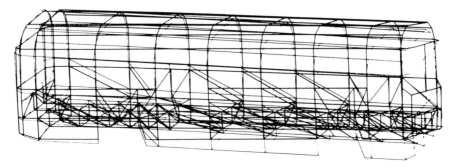

Fig. 13.13 Calculated deformation of the model bus structure shown in Fig. 13.2 in torsion, displacements in an enlarged scale

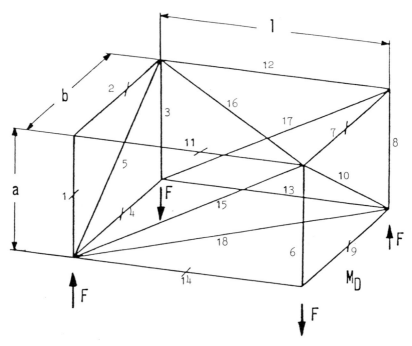

Fig. 13.14 Hollow box girder framework in torsion. Beams with zero load shown crossed

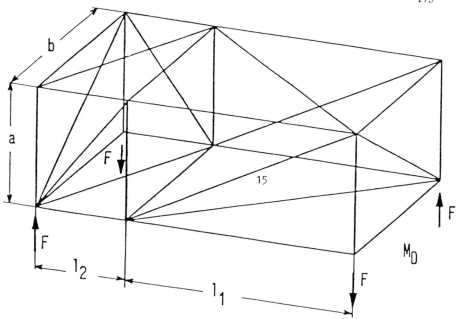

Fig. 13.15   Two bays of a hollow box framework

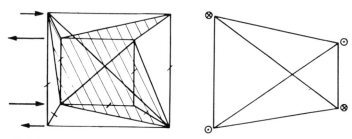

Fig. 13.16   Tapered framework in torsion. Beams with zero load shown crossed;
projection of area enclosed by load carrying members shown hatched

The relative values of the loads in the load carrying members are

$$N_{15}l/l_a = -N_{16}l/l_b = N_{12} = -N_{17}l/l_a = N_{13} = -N_{18}l/l_b \quad (13.37)$$

The torque has to be carried by the lateral components of the loads in these members, thus, taking a reference point in the centre of each cross section

$$-N_{15}\frac{a}{l_a}\cdot\frac{b}{2} + N_{16}\frac{b}{l_b}\cdot\frac{a}{2} + N_{17}\frac{a}{l_a}\cdot\frac{b}{2} + N_{18}\frac{b}{l_b}\cdot\frac{a}{2} = M_D \quad (13.38)$$

But from equation (13.36)

$$N_{16} = -N_{15}l_b/l_a; \quad N_{17} = -N_{15}; \quad N_{18} = -N_{15}l_b/l_a \quad (13.39)$$

These are inserted into equation (13.37) to give

$$N_{15}(-4/l_a) = 2M_D/ab; \quad N_{15} = -M_Dl_{15}/2A_{ab} \quad (13.40)$$

This can be expressed as a simple rule: the direct loads of the load carrying side plane members are equal to their length multiplied by the torque and divided by twice the area of the cross-section plane. This rule is somewhat parallel to Bredt's first formula. The loads in the members in the cross section plane then follow from equilibrium conditions.

In the underfloor structure several bays are joined together, as shown in the example of two bays in Fig. 13.15. These frameworks are statically determinate if there are diagonals in only two of the cross-section planes.

In practical designs these hollow frameworks may be tapered, with parallel cross-section planes of different size as in Fig. 13.16. It can be shown that, as a general rule

$$N_m = M_{DB}l_m/2A_m \quad (13.40)$$

where l_m is the length of an individual member, M_{DB} is the torque acting on the underfloor structure, and A_m is the projected area normal to the torsion axis enclosed by the load carrying members. This area is shown shaded in the figure. The loads in the other members are found from equilibrium conditions at each of the joints in the bay.

13.3 EFFECT OF GLAZING

Vehicle structures in general are significantly stiffened by window glass because of its great shear stiffness. This is particularly true for buses where there are large, plane, window areas in the side walls. The Youngs modulus of glass is 7.1×10^4 N/mm^2, which is the same as aluminium, but the Poissons ratio of glass is 0.14, which is less than that of aluminium, so that the shear modulus of 3.1×10^4 N/mm^2 is higher than that for aluminium; see reference **(14)**. The shear deformation of a 6 mm thick glass window pane can therefore be neglected compared to that of the window frame. The attachment of the glass, therefore, determines the way the shear is shared between the glass and the frame. It is easier to evaluate the effect of glass attached by adhesives than when traditional rubber mouldings are used.

Figure 13.17 shows a cross section of the attachment of a window glass by adhesive. The shear-carrying area of the adhesive is bd, but assembly techniques usually result in additional adhesive being left between the edge of the glass and frame. Only the essential principles of the shear-carrying mechanism detailed in reference **(2)** are repeated in this section,

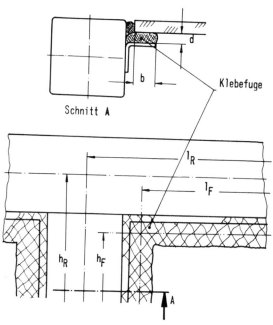

Fig. 13.17 Detail of bonded glazing.
Schnitte = cross section
Klebefuge = adhesive

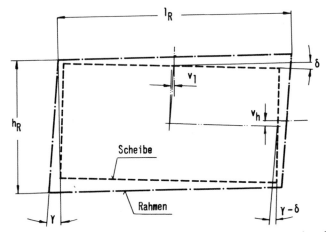

Fig. 13.18   Relative displacement of glass and frame under lozenging shear.
Scheibe = glass
Rahmen = frame

and the reader should refer to that reference for a full treatment. It is assumed that when the frame is in shear, as shown in Fig. 13.11, it will deflect as a parallelogram while the glass pane will rotate as a rigid body, as illustrated in Fig. 13.18. If the shear angle of the frame is γ and the rotation of the glass pane is δ, the adhesive joint is subject to a shear rotation of $\gamma - \delta$. The adhesive is also stretched along its length by the displacements v_l and v_h. The angle of rotation, δ, of the glass can be found from equilibrium conditions using the shear properties of the adhesive. The bending moment distribution along the members making up the window frame will be 'S' shaped, and this effect must be superimposed on the usual linear distribution when calculating the stresses in the frame for comparison with experimental measurements.

The shear-carrying capacity of the window can always be approximated by equivalent imaginary pin-jointed diagonal members of the same material as the main structure. The cross sectional area, A_d, of the equivalent members is given by the somewhat unwieldy expression

$$A_d = \frac{G_F}{E}\, \frac{b}{4d} \left(\frac{l_F h_F}{l_R h_R}\right)^2 - \frac{l_F^2 + (10/3)l_F h_F + h_F^2}{(l_F + h_F)^3} (l_R^2 + h_R^2)^{3/2} \quad (13.42)$$

where E is Youngs modulus of the structural material and G_F is the shear modulus of the adhesive. This can be given a slightly higher value than the quoted figure for the adhesive itself because of the additional adhesive noted when discussing Fig. 13.17; the other dimensions quoted in the equation are also shown in this figure.

Figure 13.19 shows the bending moments in the window and door pillars of the two sides of a bus in torsion, calculated using imaginary diagonal members, with their effective cross-section area given by the formula for A_d, to carry the shear over the window openings. It should be noted that this method does not include the 'S' shaped bending moments in the frame members because the imaginary diagonal members are treated as pin jointed. However, the maximum values of the bending moments, which occur at the ends of the pillars, will still be correct. In vertical bending the effect on the bending moments in the columns including the glazing is negligible.

The accuracy of the above method of analysis was verified by experiment on a bus side wall with the windows attached by adhesive. It was also established that the bending moments in the pillars when rubber mouldings were used to retain the glass were approximately half those measured when adhesive glazing was used.

The dynamic behaviour of adhesives is complex and the shear modulus can reach a multiple of the quasi-static value at high frequencies. Several expensive simulation models are available to analyse the viscoelastic behaviour of adhesives and these are described in reference (3).

13.4 DYNAMIC ANALYSIS

When the static analysis of a bus structure has been carried out using a framework of end-load-carrying members it is a sufficient simplification to use a lumped mass assumption for the dynamic analysis, with the masses concentrated at the joints. The mass matrix of equation (1.3) then becomes a diagonal matrix, and the stiffness matrix is already available from the static analysis, even though it may be necessary to verify it experimentally. To find the dynamic characteristics of the whole structure it has been proved that it is sufficient to idealize the metal skin by thin shell elements using a rough discretization only fixed to the framework at the joints. The mass of the skin can be added to the masses already concentrated at the joints.

The eigenfrequencies and mode shapes of a complex structure of this

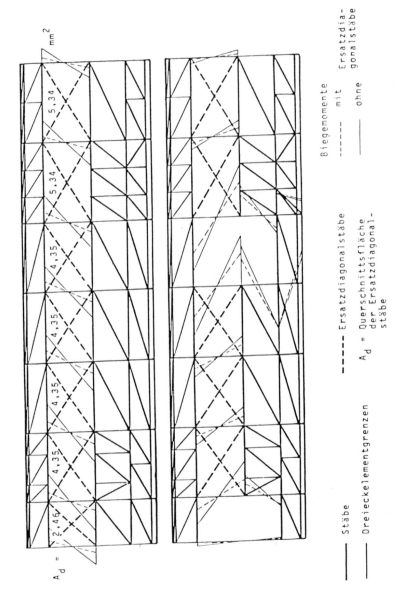

$A_d =$ 2,46 4,35 4,35 4,35 4,35 4,35 5,34 5,34 mm^2

Stäbe
Dreieckelementgrenzen

$----$ Ersatzdiagonalstäbe
$A_d =$ Querschnittsfläche der Ersatzdiagonalstäbe

Biegemomente
$------$ mit Ersatzdiagonalstäbe
$-------$ ohne gonalstäbe

Fig. 13.19

kind are best found using standard dynamic programs. These require that the structure be supported, and, since the natural frequencies of the suspension may occur in the same range as those of the structure, the supports must have dynamic properties equivalent to those of the suspension. This equivalence is best obtained if the suspension is represented by tyre springs, axle masses, road springs, and dampers. Other masses may also be connected to the structure by springs representing flexible mountings which can be simulated by pin-jointed rods of appropriate stiffness. Apart from the coupled frequencies of the suspended structure, there are usually several purely structural frequencies close to one another. For instance the structure shown in Fig. 13.3, when fully skinned, has six eigenfrequencies below 30 Hz. The mode shape of one of these frequencies is illustrated in Fig. 13.20, it can be seen that this case is mainly a torsional vibration.

When considering forced oscillations, the effect of damping must be included in the analysis. It is always sufficiently accurate to assume equivalent viscous damping characteristics whatever the actual damping process may be. It is also desirable to simplify the analysis, either by reducing the number of degrees of freedom by reducing the number of mass points, or by using a modal formulation for the problem. Modal formulation consists of limiting the number of mode shapes considered. These are defined as generalized coordinates which are arranged as columns in the modal matrix, $\mathbf{X}$. The column matrix of the generalised displacements, $\mathbf{q}$, is related to the displacements of the nodes, $\mathbf{d}$, by

$$\mathbf{d} = \mathbf{X}\mathbf{q} \tag{13.43}$$

Substituting this into equation (1.3) and premultiplying by $\mathbf{X}^T$, the following equation is obtained

$$\mathbf{X}^T\mathbf{M}\mathbf{X}\ddot{\mathbf{q}} + \mathbf{X}^T\mathbf{C}\mathbf{X}\dot{\mathbf{q}} + \mathbf{X}^T\mathbf{K}\mathbf{X}\mathbf{q} = \mathbf{X}^T\mathbf{f}(t)$$

Fig. 13.19 Example showing the reduction of bending moment in door and window pillars due to the use of substitute imaginary diagonal beams in place of bonded glazing in the side walls of a bus under torsion. [Stäbe = actual beams; Dreieckelementgrenzen = boundary of triangular element used for FE analysis; Ersatzdiagonalstäbe = substitute beams; A_d = cross section area of substitute beams; Biegemomente = bending moment; mit = with; ohne = without.]

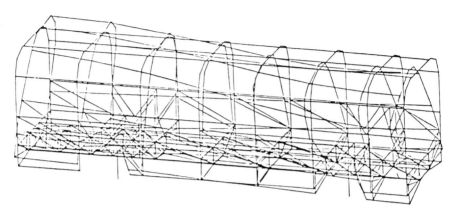

Fig. 13.20   Example of a calculated mode shape of the model bus structure with metal skinning

or

$$M_q\ddot{q} + C_q\dot{q} + K_qq = f_q(t) \qquad (13.44)$$

where M_q is the generalized mass matrix, C_q the generalized damping matrix, K_q the generalized stiffness matrix, and $f_q(t)$ the generalized external loads, as in

$$M_q = X^TMX \quad C_q = X^TCX$$
$$K_q = X^TKX \quad f_q = X^Tf \qquad (13.45)$$

Because the modal matrix is orthogonal, all the other matrices are diagonal, so that the equations of motion are decoupled, with attendant advantages.

The nodal points can be arranged together in statically equivalent groups to reduce the number of mass points in the idealization to simplify the analysis. A sufficiently accurate approximation can usually be achieved by this method, when there are just sufficient mass points to define geometrically all the mode shapes in the frequency range of interest.

The Guyan condensation method should be used in preference to the above simplification scheme if it is available in the software system used for the dynamic analysis, because it is mechanically more accurate. In this method the so-called master degrees of freedom, d_1, are chosen from the original nodal point displacements, $\mathbf{d}$, and the forces corresponding to the remaining displacements, $\mathbf{d}_2$, are set at zero. $\mathbf{d}$ is partitioned as

$$\mathbf{d} = \begin{bmatrix} \mathbf{d}_1 \\ \hline \mathbf{d}_2 \end{bmatrix} \qquad (13.46)$$

Dynamic displacements occur in the master degrees of freedom which induce motion in the remaining, so-called, 'condensed away' components because of the elastic connection within the structure. The condensed mass matrix is then obtained using the kinetic energy of these approximate displacements.

The stiffness matrix will be partitioned in accordance with equation (13.45) into

$$\mathbf{K} = \begin{bmatrix} \mathbf{K}_{11} & \mathbf{K}_{12} \\ \hline \mathbf{K}_{21} & \mathbf{K}_{22} \end{bmatrix} \qquad (13.47)$$

so that the condensed stiffness matrix becomes

$$\mathbf{K}_c = \mathbf{K}_{11} - \mathbf{K}_{12}\mathbf{K}_{22}^{-1}\mathbf{K}_{21} \qquad (13.48)$$

and, with a corresponding partition of the lumped mass matrix, the condensed mass matrix becomes

$$\mathbf{M}_c = \mathbf{M}_{11} + (\mathbf{K}_{22}^{-1}\mathbf{K}_{21})^{\mathrm{T}}\mathbf{M}_{22}(\mathbf{K}_{22}^{-1}\mathbf{K}_{21}) \qquad (13.49)$$

References

(1) **Argyris, J. H.** Die Matrizentheorie der Statik, *Ing.-Archiv*, 1957, **25**, S. 74–192.

(2) **Beermann, H. J.** Die Auswirkung der Seitenwandverglasung auf die Trageigenschaften von Omnibusstrukturen, XVII FISITA-Kongreß, 1978. Budapest.

(3) **Beermann, H. J. and Gohrbandt, U.** Dynamisches Verhalten der Klebung von Fahrzeugverglasungen, *Autom. Industrie*, **1979**, Heft 4, S. 61–64.

(4) **Beermann, H. J. and Gohrbandt, U.** Berechnung der Torsion von Nutzfahrzeugrahmen mit geschlossenen Querträgern, *Fortschrittberichte VDI Z Reihe*, 1, Nr. 61, 1979.

(5) **Erz, K.** Uber durch Unebenheiten der Fahrbahn hervorgerufene Verdrehung von Straßenfahrzeugen, *Automtechn. Zeitschr.*, 1957, Heft 4, S. 89–95; Heft 6, S. 163–170.

(6) **Gallagher, R. H.** *Finite element analysis*, Berlin, Heidelberg, New York, 1976.

(7) **Kersten, R.** *Das Reduktionsverfahren der Baustatik*, Berlin, Göttingen, Heidelberg, 1962.

(8) **Kollbrunner, C. F., and Hajdin, N.** *Dünnwandige Stäbe*, Berlin, Heidelberg, 1972.

(9) **Marótzy, M.** *Gekröpfte Leiterrahmen (ungarisch)*, Dissertation, Budapest, 1981.

(10) **Mitschke, M.** *Dynamik der Kraftfahrzeuge*, Berlin, 1982.

(11) **Oehlschlaeger, H.** *Berechnung verwindungsweicher Nutzfahrzeugrahmen auf Torsion unter Berücksichtigung der Knotenausbildung*, Dissertation, TU Braunschweig, 1981.

(12) **Przemieniecki, J. S.** *Theory of Matrix Structural Analysis*, New York, 1968.

(13) **Roik, K., Carl, J., and Lindner, J.** *Biegetorsionsprobleme gerader dünnwandiger Stäbe*, Berlin, München, Düsseldorf, 1972.

(14) **Stevels, J. M.** The Structure and Physical Properties of Glass, in *Handbuch der Physik*, Berlin, Göttingen, Heidelberg, 1962.

(15) **Wlassow, W. S.** *Dünnwandige elastische Stäbe*, Berlin, 1964.

(16) **Weaver, W. and Gere, J. M.** *Matrix Analysis of Framed Structures*, New York, 1980.

(17) **Beermann, H. J.** Static analysis of commercial vehicle frames: A hybrid–finite element and analytical–method, *Int. J. Vehicle Des.*, 1984, **5**, 26–52.

(18) **Beermann, H. J.** Joint deformations and stresses of commercial vehicle frame under torsion, *Vehicle Structures*, IMechE, London, 1984.

Index